Don't You Get It?

Living With
Auditory Learning Disabilities

Harvey Edell

Jay R. Lucker, Ed.D., CCC-A/SLP, FAAA

Loraine Alderman, Psy.D.

Shadow Publishing
2008

Contributions by:

Andrew Alderman
Carmela Granata Bernacchio
Danielle Carmela Lisanti

Library of Congress Cataloging in Publication Data
Shadow Publishing
ISBN: 0-9675434-1-X
Printed in the United States of America

Table of Contents

Acknowledgement

Our Heartfelt thanks must be acknowledged in print to Barbara Harrington for her invaluable advice and editing of this book.

A thank you must also be said to our spouses, family and friends for their feedback, patience and understanding during the writing of this book.

Harvey, Jay and Loraine

Forward
by Jack Katz, Ph.D.

As you may already know auditory processing problems can cause significant difficulty in communication and academics. But if you are not sufficiently aware of exactly what an Auditory Processing Disorder (APD) is or what impact it may have on the person and their family then, *"Don't You Get It? Living with Auditory Learning Disabilities"* was written for you. This book not only covers what APD is and how to test for it, but also discusses how to treat the problems that are uncovered. However, uniquely this book also lets you hear the stories, insights and suggestions of those who have personally dealt with and minimize this problem.

It is important to know about APD because there is so much that can be done to alleviate it and to improve these abilities. It is also important because of the widespread misinformation, or lack of information, that causes too many people to needlessly suffer the continued consequences of APD.

One of the biggest problems facing those who have APD is that not enough parents and professionals know that it exists and also that it is not difficult to diagnose it – even in young children – and effective compensations and therapies are available which permit children and adults with this problem to make major strides in overcoming its effects. Thus, those who read this book can not only help themselves and/or loved ones, but can serve others in helping to erase some of the misinformation, clarify vague concepts, and illuminate APD for those who are not aware that it is right here in our midst.

Don't You Get It? Living with Auditory Learning Disabilities provides information about the nature of this disorder from a leader in APD for many years and discusses what the central tests and therapy procedures can offer. Dr. Jay Lucker also discusses classroom management strategies that can ease the burden of those with APD. This book is written in an easy to read, informal style that should appeal to parents and professionals alike.

I too have dealt with APD all of my life, but when I was a child there was no concept of auditory processing problems, so children were thought to be too lazy to learn (as I was considered) while I myself thought that I was mentally retarded because of my consistent failure to learn. But I was fortunate because we were not taught to read until second grade and taught to spell even after that. Nowadays the demands on children are greater and earlier in life, so the consequences are more severe. We cannot afford to let children continue to fall through the cracks because of the many negative consequences to the individual, their family, their school and to society.

It is my hope that you will use what you learn from those who have made their way out of the confines imposed by APD and encourage others that this need not be a life-long sentence. When those who are resistant to the concept of APD hear from enough people who have been helped, let's hope they too will "Get It" and help rather than ignore this important problem.

Chapter One

Don't You Get It?

An Introduction

by Jay R. Lucker Ed.D., CCC-A/SLP, FAAA

If you or someone you know has (APD), an Auditory Process-ing Disorder sometimes called a central Auditory Process-ing Disorder (CAPD), also described as an Auditory Information Processing Disorders (APD) (Lucker 2005a), this book can give you the answers to the many questions. Two of the most often asked questions about APD are: 'What is it like to have the disorder?' and 'Can a person overcome it?' This book provides insights into both of these questions.

It has been estimated that three to five percent of children have APD with an unknown percent of them continuing to have prob-lems processing auditory information into adulthood (Geffner & Ross-Swain, 2007). In a research project looking at auditory informa-tion processing abilities in children identified with specific learning disabilities (SLD), this author found that over half failed tests of auditory processing. Thus, over 50% of those children with learning problems have some difficulties processing auditory information.

The number of adults with APD is unidentified because less focus has been placed on testing auditory information processing problems in adults. As we are still learning to recognize APDs and differentiate them from other disorders such as AD/HD, attention deficit disorders, we struggle as professionals and specialists in the area of auditory processing to identify exactly *what is* and *what is not* an auditory processing deficit. We do know and recognize that both children and adults have APD, and that there are a variety of factors that account for the problems people may experience when processing what they hear. *(For a better understanding of APD, see Chapter Two.)*

APD is most readily identified in children, and, as you will see from cases presented in this book, it affects their education, socialization, but most importantly, their self-esteem. However, there is help today. Children with APD, as well as adults, can learn to overcome their processing difficulties either by developing improved ways to process what they hear or by learning strategies to compensate for the difficulties APD can present. Additionally, as APD is becoming better recognized and understood, people are beginning to receive help in many countries throughout the world. (See the APDUK website on the internet at **www.apduk.org.**)

A number of popular books have been written about APD. One discusses what it is like to be a parent struggling to understand her child's auditory processing problems (Foli, 2003). Another is written by a professional who discusses APD from a very technical perspective, though her book is understandable by parents, teachers, and people with APD (Bellis, 2003). A recent publication is written primarily for professionals but understood by anyone. In this book, there is an entire chapter presenting sample reports from professionals regarding APD issues in children that provide the reader with insights into how different children perform on various measures used to assess APD as well as providing some recommendations to help these children (Geffner & Ross-Swain, 2007).

Until now, there has not been a book that specifically looks at how people with APD have lived and learned to overcome the disorder from childhood into adulthood. This book was written by those people who have lived with APD their entire lives. Their contributions include data by professionals who are involved in the assessment, treatment, and education of children, adolescents, and adults with APD.

Additionally, the experiences of an adolescent, a young adult, and their mothers are included. This book will provide the reader with insights into how they struggled and overcame their APD problems, with a focus on what elements helped them succeed. These adults and children will convince you that APD is something that *can* be overcome with the right support.

The technical information in this book is presented by a professional who has worked for over 30 years in the area of APD. He has been engaged in research as well as being involved in clinical practice assessing APD issues with a focus to provide treatments for children and adults with auditory information processing problems as well as offering consultations and support to anyone with an interest in APD. He has also presented numerous APD workshops and seminars, and is the president, chair of the board, and co-founder of the National Coalition on Auditory Processing Disorders, Inc. **(www.ncapd.org).**

The authors who discuss their true life APD encounters include Harvey Edell, who has lived with problems processing auditory-linguistic information for over 60 years; his daughter, Loraine, a school psychologist, who has APD issues and works with school children having auditory based learning problems as well as being the mother of a child with APD; and her teenage son, Andrew who has APD, and contributes reflections about his life experiences with his disorders.

Another contributor, a professional woman with two children with APD, Carmela Bernacchio, the director of a center that focuses on treating communication and learning problems including those related to children and adults with APD problems, presents her own story as well as having one of her daughters reflect on her personal problems.

These six people have lived with and successfully overcome difficulties because of auditory information processing problems. They discuss how APD affects them now and how it affected them when they were young. Their insights provide perspectives for people who deal with or have APD.

You will find common themes throughout the individual stories. One important theme is to learn how each person felt having problems processing auditory-linguistic information. Another important one is how each person overcame his or her problems including what factors helped him or her deal with APD and related issues. Identifying these themes can help you understand what you can do to help yourself or the person you know who has APD.

These stories are brought together to demonstrate the common threads woven into the lives of people who live everyday with APD.

This book provides you with a better understanding of what are auditory information processing disorders including various definitions and models developed that are used by professionals. Reviewing these models, you will better understand which professionals assess and diagnose people with such problems, and how these professionals work to differentiate between APD and other problems that look like APD, such as attention disorders and language difficulties. The book also provides an overview of how APD is assessed including actual data and interpretations from sample cases.

One chapter focuses on treating APD and what can be done to help children with APD problems. Discussions focus on treatments that some of the contributors to this book have undergone. The concluding chapter presents resources that include organizations, support systems, and how to find professionals who provide assessments and treatments of auditory information processing deficits. You will identify that APD is not debilitating and it can be overcome.

Chapter Two

What are Auditory Information Processing Disorders?

by Jay R. Lucker Ed.D., CCC-A/SLP, FAAA

Auditory Information Processing Disorders (APD) involve deficits related to a person having difficulty:

1. taking in information through their auditory systems (all parts of their ears),

2. getting that information to the brain (via the auditory pathways and related or interconnected pathways in the central nervous system),

3. forming meaningful mental images of that information in order to comprehend the meaning of the message and act appropriately (Lucker 2005a, 2007a).

A generic definition of an auditory information processing disorder could be a *disorder in understanding spoken language due to an imperfect ability to listen.* This definition of APD is cited from the definition of a specific learning disability in the special education law known as the Individuals with Disabilities Education Act or IDEA. Many people refer to these deficits as Auditory Processing Disorders (APD), central Auditory Processing Disorders (CAPD), and (central) Auditory Processing Disorders ((C)APD). Medwetsky (2006) coined the term *Spoken Language Processing Disorder* for APD in order to expand the terminology to be in line with what people *actually* see when a person has problems processing spoken language.

Lucker (2005a, 2007a) expanded the broader view of APD taken by Medwetsky to take in not only the processing of spoken language, but the processing of any auditory information whether linguistic or nonlinguistic (such as understanding the meaning of someone knocking on a door). Using the plural for the name indicates that it is a spectrum of disorders or, rather, various categories of processing that can breakdown in the total process of taking in information through the auditory system.

In 2007(a), Lucker described APD as involving five different systems, not just the auditory system as is the common approach among professionals (Jerger and Musiek, 2000; ASHA, 2005a; Geffner, 2007). It is Lucker's approach to APD that was used in assessing the cases presented in this book.

Many people believe that APD is a recently identified disorder. A review of the history of APD in children (Lucker, 2007b) indicates that the first publications that specifically discussed problems that children without hearing loss have in processing auditory information were in books published in the mid-to-late 1950s.

In 1969, a monograph published through the National Institutes of Health first presented the term central auditory dysfunction in children to describe APD (Chalfant and Scheffelin 1969). About 10 years later, at the first national, professional conference on APD, the name was changed to Central Auditory Processing Disorder or CAPD and that label stuck until the 1990s (see Keith, 1977). In the fall of 2007, a second conference was held, sponsored by Dr. Keith, to provide a 30 year update. **(see: www.apdcincinnati. com/faculty1.php)**

During the 1990s, a number of professionals argued that the use of "central" in CAPD argued that it was a disorder of the central auditory nervous system (CANS) was too limiting since much of the research did not support a CANS focal disorder in children with APD. In 2000, Jerger and Musiek recommended the term APD to replace the older term CAPD. Then, in 2005, the Technical Report from the Committee on Auditory Processing Disorders of the American Speech-Language-Hearing Association (ASHA) called the disorder a (Central) Auditory Processing Disorder or (C)APD. However, whether you call the disorder CAPD, APD, or (C)APD, we are all discussing disorders that lead to problems making sense out of the information received via the ear and brain that eventually leads to the comprehension of that information. In 2005, 2007, Lucker proposed the broader term, Auditory Information Processing Disorder, continuing the use of the initials APD.

Approaches to APD

Not only is there disagreement as to terminology used to name this disorder, there are different approaches and definitions professionals have as to what they call APD.

The traditional approach to APD takes one of three paths. One path may be referred to as the "test battery approach" or the "Pass/Fail model." In this approach, APD is determined by giving a child a battery of APD tests, then determining whether the child passed or failed specific tests. It is then concluded that the child does not have or does have an APD. Some professionals using this "Pass/Fail" approach may go further to describe the specific tests on which the person failed. For example, if a child failed a test of understanding speech in the presence of noise, the professional might state that "Today's testing supports a conclusion that Johnny has an APD with problems understanding speech in noise." The professional might go further describing how problems understanding speech in noise could affect Johnny, and even provide suggestions for helping Johnny cope better with speech presented in noise.

There is one problem with that approach. Because there could be many reasons why a child would have problems understanding speech in the presence of the noise, there is no specific identification as to *why* Johnny has such problems. Thus, unless you can identify the *why* of the behavior, you cannot appropriately approach treating the problem.

One possible factor for Johnny having problems with speech understanding in noise is that he can't focus on the speaker because he cannot both focus and filter out the noise at the same time. Thus, the noise becomes an auditory distracter. Another factor could be that the noise masked out auditory cues from the relevant speech message distorting the message, and Johnny cannot make sense of the distortion. A third factor is one related to an attention problem. Johnny cannot appropriately choose to what he must attend and the noise seems more interesting than the teacher speaking. Treating Johnny for an auditory distractibility problem when the problem is one of the other two described above is not appropriate.

If Johnny's problem is noise distractibility, we need to remove the distractions as well as teach him how to be less distracted. Such intervention would not necessarily help a child who is not really distracted by the noise but does not know how to appropriately attend to the primary speaker. For the child who has problems understanding the message in quiet as well as in noise, removing the noise will not make him better able to understand the primary message. Helping him better understand messages even in quiet is the appropriate treatment.

One of the major weaknesses of the "Pass/Fail" model is that it does not seek to identify what is really at the foundation of the problem. Therefore, appropriate interventions may not be identified.

A second approach to APD is what can be referred to as a neuro-physiological approach. This seems to be the most common approach used in research being conducted on auditory information processing today. This perspective involves two factors. One is that young children's central auditory nervous systems or CANS undergo a great deal of normal maturation until a specific age. This age is usually identified as around 12 years. Thus, any child failing APD tests prior to the age of 12 is diagnosed as having either an immature central auditory system or has developmental problems that need us to wait and watch to see whether normal auditory system development occurs in early adolescence.

Many of the professionals holding this approach identify the lowest age at which children can be tested for APD to be around seven. (Katz, 2005; Lucker, 2005b) Thus, parents are told they cannot have their child tested until age seven, or that the results of APD testing merely identifies their child having an immature system.

For some professionals taking a neurophysiological approach, the focus is to identify where in the CANS the disorder occurs. For example, a report reviewed by the author stated that a child might have a disorder in his auditory brainstem pathways leading from the auditory nerve or eighth nerve to the upper brainstem on the way to the brain. The evaluator, not the author, referred the child for tests to identify the presence of brainstem pathology. The author was consulted to review the data and found that there was no support to identify this child as having a possible brainstem tumor or problem such as multiple sclerosis or ALS. In contrast, the boy had problems with auditory distractibility needing work to improve his abilities to focus on the primary speaker and learn to ignore the noise.

Follow-up with a pediatric neurotologist (ear doctor who specializes in disorders of the nerves and brain) revealed absolutely no abnormalities for this boy. Thus, after hundreds of dollars have been spent, the parents and the school district were still at the same point they were when the initial referral for the APD assessment was made. This led to referring the child for a second opinion. Based on this author's interpretation, the child was offered accommodations and treatment and, eventually, improved his abilities to listen in noise and was able to function successfully in the regular education setting.

This case presentation does not mean that APD cannot be due to neurological disorders. It is possible for children to have had head injuries or other neurological problems, such as tumors. However, there would be various signs from both the case history and test findings to support such interpretation that a child may have some neurological problem. In such a case, referral to an appropriate specialist would be recommended. Care is needed for the professional interpreting APD test findings not to jump to conclusions based on one or two behavioral tests that a person might have a neurological disorder.

The author was once asked to see a young male adolescent who was one year post treatment for encephalitis. His presenting problems included seizure disorder, loss of language after hospitalization for encephalitis, and loss of "listening skills." Prior to his becoming ill he was among the top 10th percentile in middle school, was in the gifted and talented (G/T) program, and was advanced in many academic areas. Because he was assessed for the G/T program, it was known that his IQ was at the higher end of the normal range and his academic achievement was above grade level. After contracting the encephalitis, he lost his language comprehension abilities, his abilities to speak, and his abilities to listen. When he was released from the hospital and the encephalitis had been treated, he had seizures and continued to have problems with comprehension of what was said to him. Interestingly, he was able to read and comprehend what he read. It was as if his auditory system might have been affected by the encephalitis.

Speech-language therapy, as well as other treatments, were provided for one year. Yet, he persisted to have listening and comprehension problems. The author saw him upon referral to test for APD. The findings, as well as the case history, suggested there may be neurological problems unidentified affecting the auditory system. MRI studies ordered by the boy's physician showed the problems in the auditory areas of his brain. Having this insight helped in treatment as well as having both the boy and his parents better understand why the boy was not progressing in listening and comprehension. The greatest advantage was the family coming to a more realistic acceptance of how much their son might progress.

The analysis of the boy's APD test findings indicated auditory extraction problems at the speech sound or phonemic level and at the linguistic or lexical level. Thus, he was not able to pull out the auditory information that differentiated phonemes leading to severe problems with auditory discrimination and to pull out the key words from linguistic messages leading to him not to be able to remember what was spoken to him as well as misinterpreting what was said. Treatment began with a neuropsychologist who provided therapy working largely on auditory discrimination, auditory phonemic awareness, and temporal (time) processing such as using the time differences between words that differentiate one word from two words (i.e., 'hot dog' from 'hotdog'). One year after treatment, the young man regained a great deal of lost language, academic, communication, and listening abilities.

The third approach to APD is a categorical approach in which the professional assesses auditory information processing and identifies specific APD categories. The categories include both the APD strengths and weaknesses as well as what interventions are needed to improve processing within the deficient categories.

One popular categorical approach is called the Buffalo Model developed by Dr. Jack Katz and his associates (Katz, 1992). This approach identifies four major categories and some subcategories, such as Integration Type I and Type II. The categories are based on specific indicators from APD tests.

Another categorical approach is that developed by the author (2005a, 2007a & b, 2008). It also looks at specific test findings as well as case history data and behaviors observed during testing, especially analysis of error patterns on test items. The purpose of this approach is to identify in what specific categories the child is functioning poorly. Descriptions of each category lead to the specific skills needed to process normally in that category. Interventions are then focused on teaching the skills or strategies to overcome the deficits found in each category.

For example, consider the adolescent described above with encephalitis. Test findings and behaviors during testing indicated that he was better able to process visually than auditorily. Thus, one focus of treatment was to teach him various visual strategies, such as speechreading (sometimes called lipreading) to discriminate words he heard. Another strategy was to use cognitive thinking skills to figure out the meaning of verbal messages based on the context, the words understood, and other metacognitive strategies.

The categorical approach proposes that there are specific individual categories that differentiate between types of APDs.

What Should I Do as a Parent or Educator?

Auditory information processing is being approached differently by professionals. Thus, it is important that both parents and educators ask professionals dealing with people who have APD to explain their description of APD and the approach they take in assessment and interpretation.

Many professionals view APD in accordance with the ASHA Technical report of 2005. In that report, auditory processing is described as involving activity in the auditory neural pathways leading to specific skills such as auditory discrimination, localization, understanding speech in the presence of background noise, auditory memory, etc. Yet, many of these professionals do not assess all of the skills described in the ASHA report. For example, there are no standardized clinical tests of auditory localization at the time of this writing, yet localization is one of the ASHA identified skills. Additionally, a focus of assessment is often related to auditory temporal processing or making judgments about time factors related to sounds such as how may sounds a child hears when shorter and shorter gaps between the sounds are present. There is no research that supports that deficits in auditory temporal processing of noises and sounds is related to any specific skills in understanding verbal messages. Therefore, focusing on tests of temporal processing does not provide insights into why Johnny cannot learn in school.

Another problem identified with the ASHA description of auditory processing skills is that all of the skills described require a high level of processing from systems that have nothing to do with the ear or auditory centers of the brain. For example, auditory discrimination, the ability to distinguish whether two sounds or words are the same or different, relies heavily on memory, attention, and decision making all cognitive, not auditory, processes. Furthermore, brain centers for memory, attention, and decision making have no locations within the auditory pathways in the brain. Thus, Lucker (2005a, 2007a, 2008) proposed that auditory information processing involves more than just the auditory system. It involves five distinct systems that work together in an integrated manner to produce the end result, comprehension of the sounds and words we hear.

As can be seen above, auditory information processing involves not only the auditory system but also the cognitive system. Cognition is a field of psychology that deals with thinking and related processes (including memory, attention, concentration, and self-regulation of behavior). Many children this professional sees for APD assessments actually have primary deficits in cognitive areas, not auditory based problems. However, the cognitive deficits lead to problems processing what they hear, thus, they are identified by this author as having APD due to primary cognitive deficits. Therefore, intervention for these children must focus on the cognitive problems, not auditory issues.

A Different Perspective On APD

Lucker's approach (2005a, 2007a, 2008) to APD is much broader than that taken by most professionals. It is more in line with Medwetsky's description (2006), but goes even further. The people presented in the book were assessed for APD and identified as having APD using Lucker's approach.

This approach defines auditory information processing as those things (i.e., processes) involved when the entire central nervous system receives information one hears, and gets that information to the brain where it eventually forms meaningful 'mental images.' In those processes, the meaningful mental image is placed into memory for later recall or a cognitive determination is made to respond to the information or ignore it. Once the mental images have been formed, language or linguistic labels are placed on the images and their parts to allow for manipulation of the information including formulating a concept for future recall or responding to questions asked of the listener.

This approach involves the integrative balance of five systems: the auditory system, the cognitive system, the behavioral-emotional system, the language system, and the sensory-regulatory system. Thus, a child could have a problem with APD due to a deficit in one or more of these systems or with the appropriate integration between these systems.

Lucker proposes that most children with APD do not have primary auditory problems. Instead, children may have auditory based deficits or problems in other systems, such as problems with attention (a factor involving the behavioral-emotional system). The focus of assessment then is to evaluate all systems and identify which ones may be contributing to the primary deficits. Consider the following two cases.

A young girl with a primary sensory-regulatory problem comes in for APD assessment. She has difficulties appropriately using sensory information to process her world. When asked to sit and listen, she is not sure that she is sitting properly or falling down, so she wonders where she is in space. When sitting on a couch, for example, her feet are not on the floor, and she wonders if she is floating in space or firmly sitting down. All she can think about is not falling off. How much energy will she have to listen? Very little, if any! Thus, her lack of listening leads people to wonder whether she has APD.

When she comes in for the APD assessment, she is seated on a chair that does not allow her feet to firmly touch the ground. She spends the entire time wondering whether she will fall rather than listening carefully to the messages she is hearing. She fails the APD testing. Should she be diagnosed with APD?

The author did describe her as having APD problems due to primary sensory-regulation difficulties. Recommendations for treatment focused on sensory regulation processes and not on auditory or language treatments. This is a major difference between Lucker's approach to APD and the generally accepted one.

Now imagine a boy in a similar situation. When he is told to sit and listen, he is impatiently waiting for the next thing to be said to him. He interrupts the speaker asking seemingly irrelevant questions. Again, people watching him note he has problems listening and wonder whether it is APD.

This boy comes in for APD testing. After only a few items are presented on a test, he wants to know whether the test is finished. He stops listening and starts looking at the toys or wires in the evaluation room. He fails the tests. Does he have APD?

He definitely has problems processing what he hears because he is not always available to listen. He was found to have attention problems that may be due to something like AD/HD. Yet, he does have problems with APD because of the attention difficulties. For him, treatment needs to focus on the attention issues and not listening factors.

The third illustration is a boy who is also told to sit and listen. He sits and listens, but he cannot distinguish the words he hears. When the teacher says, 'This is a story about a little girl named Red Riding Hood who took a basket of food to her grandmother's house in the woods,' the boy hears 'boring' for the word 'story' and 'curl' for the word, 'girl'" He sits wondering what is boring and what is a red riding curl? He cannot follow what the teacher says, so he stops listening and starts playing with a toy he found lying on the ground. The teacher notices this behavior as typical, and wonders if he has an attention problems such as AD/HD. APD testing indicated that this boy had auditory phonemic extraction problems, i.e., difficulties with auditory discrimination and manipulating the speech sounds or phonemes he hears to form appropriate words.

In all three of these examples, the children presented with problems listening. In two cases, the adults watching the child's behaviors wondered whether there could be APD problems. In the third case, the boy actually has APD, yet the teacher thinks it might be AD/HD. Only an appropriate assessment of all systems would identify each child's problem. Providing auditory discrimination work for the third child would be appropriate, but not for the other two. Giving the last boy AD/HD medication would not improve his auditory discrimination.

APD and the Educational System

If you have or know of someone who has an APD, you may understand that processing verbal information can lead to problems in education. This factor was recognized when the original writers of the federal education law protecting children with educational disabilities was written. They identified that a disorder in understanding spoken language due to imperfect ability to listen, thus, APD, should be classified as a specific learning disability (SLD). Therefore, the definition of SLD in the education law, IDEA, is written as problems understanding spoken language (not classified as a speech-language impairment), an imperfect ability to listen, and a disorder such as an auditory perceptual disorder (a term sometimes used for APD that is still one of the medical diagnostic categories used: ICD-9-CM code 388.40 = A disorder of auditory perception). Therefore, when a child is found to have learning problems in school and the problems are due to underlying APD, the child has an SLD.

Many school districts do not recognize this simple fact. They feel that APD is not covered in the IDEA. However, as just stated, APD is defined in three different ways as one type of SLD. For the complete definition:

'The term 'specific learning disability' means a disorder in one or more of the basic psychological processes involved in *understanding* or in *using language, spoken* or written, which disorder may manifest itself in the *imperfect ability to listen*, think, speak, read, write, spell, or do mathematical calculations.'

The definition goes on to state that the term SLD:

'"....*includes such conditions as perceptual disabilities*, brain injury, minimal brain dysfunction, dyslexia, and developmental aphasia.' (Public Law 108-446, Individuals with Disabilities Education Act (IDEA), Reauthorization, December 3, 2004)

Thus, children who have difficulties learning and are found to have APD should be provided the services they need under the designation of SLD or should be eligible for services due to an SLD based on a specific APD. However, one important factor is to identify that the child is having problems learning in school with all modifications made that would normally be made for any other child without a disability.

If you have gone to your school district because of learning problems with your child, you may have found that your district does not recognize APD as an eligibility criterion. Many children struggle in school unable to understand what they hear, and many parents are told that their children find it difficult to learn because of listening difficulties. Yet, these children are found ineligible for services under IDEA by many school districts when they are identified as having APD. Often the reason is that educators do not understand APD or they view it as a disorder specific to the auditory system. Thus, if a child does not have a hearing loss the child does not have an auditory disorder. Or, they view APD as a language disorder, and the child can only have APD if the child fails language tests. This is not the case.

In a research study looking at the number of children evaluated for both auditory and language issues related to APD, this author (Lucker, 2007a, 2008) found the following:

a. A group of 90 children were seen for APD assessments in which the same comprehensive battery of auditory and language tests were administered.

b. Retrospective analysis of the outcomes from these tests identified that only 2% of these 90 children, originally referred for auditory based problems, failed only language tests and passed all of the auditory tests.

c. In contrast, 59% failed both auditory and language tests.

d. However, 39% of the total sample failed only the auditory tests and passed all of the language tests.

This research indicates that about 40% of children in the sample identified with deficits in processing auditory information only have auditory based APD. Thus, there is a large percentage of children who have auditory based problems with no language deficits and have difficulties processing auditory information. Therefore, we cannot conclude that APD is nothing more than a language disorder. However, since about 60% were found to have both auditory and language deficits accounting for their APD, we could identify many children with APD problems as being eligible for educational support services due to a specific language impairment or SLI.

For some children having auditory deficits in information processing, they are successfully able to compensate and are found to have no specific learning problems on formal, standardized testing. One example would be children who are distracted by background classroom noises and do not have attention deficits but who have difficulties following verbal messages. These children might fail tests of speech understanding because of the interfering effects of the noise. They may have problems in school understanding what the teachers are saying. Academic achievement testing and standard tests administered in quiet test rooms indicate normal findings for these children. Yet, teachers notice that the children are lost or unable to follow through on verbal messages. These children would have specific APD problems due to auditory distractibility and would benefit from treatment and accommodations. Unfortunately, many schools find them ineligible for special education support services or for a formal accommodations plan. Yet, they require accommodations and services (often called related services), that they may be able to obtain under IDEA or under Section 504 of the Rehabilitation Act. Even those with APD who are academically performing well could be eligible for help through accommodations, such as controlling noise levels, working in smaller groups, and, when appropriate, they can be provided with technology to reduce the interference of any background noise. Additionally, they can be provided with related speech-language services to teach them how to overcome their problems understanding verbal messages in noisy listening situations.

Conclusions

As the reader can see, there is much involved in understanding what are and what are not APDs. The discussions of APD in this book are based on Lucker's approach in which deficits seen could be related to one or some combination of five different systems that underly successful auditory information processing not merely just related to problems with the auditory system. The five systems include the auditory system, the cognitive system, the behavioral-emotional system, the language system, and the sensory-regulation system. Successful auditory processing is viewed as the appropriate integration in the functioning of these five systems. From a neuro-physiological view, auditory processing involves more than just the central auditory pathways in the brain. Systems involved with sensory regulation, memory, attention and emotional processing are also involved with successful auditory information processing.

Such systems may include parts of the brain such as the limbic system, the cerebellum, and the frontal lobes of the brain, none of which include primary auditory neural pathways. This approach to APD views auditory processing and APD in a much broader sense than the traditional view (ASHA, 2005a).

Understanding this perspective, the reader can look further into the lives of the people presented here and hopefully have a better understanding of theirs or their children's APD problems. Each person discussed in this book has lived with APD and learned to successfully deal with their auditory information processing problems.

As you will see in Chapter Nine, assessment of APD needs to identify the specific, underlying factors and Chapter Ten emphasizes the needs to treat problems in the specific, underlying systems, and not take a generic approach to auditory processing as is often the approach used by many professionals. Read on and find out how APD affected the lives of those presented in this book and how they struggled and worked to overcome and deal with their APD.

Chapter Three

Jay R. Lucker's Life
and School Experiences

by Jay R. Lucker Ed.D., CCC-A/SLP, FAAA

One of the factors that focused my interest in APD was growing up with the disability. When I was a child in elementary school, we did not recognize the different types of learning disabilities, and often children with learning problems were considered slow developers, late bloomers, or just plain slow. I bet teachers thought I was one of these late bloomers, but I just felt plain stupid.

When I was in elementary school, educators did not really understand auditory based learning disabilities (LDs). Although I did not do well in language based subjects in elementary and junior high school grades, I did do well in math, my favorite subject. But, when I had to deal with math word problems, I didn't like math as much.

It was a struggle for me to understand what my teachers were saying, and I often could not make sense out of how letters and sounds went together when learning phonics. I read books only because I was told to read them, but I hardly ever understood what I was reading. I'll never forget how embarrassed I felt when the kids laughed when I mispronounced words.

Reading, especially decoding, is a process that requires certain pre-reading skills. One of the most important ones is what is called auditory phonemic awareness. This skill relates to the ability one has to mentally manipulate the sounds in words (called phonemes). We manipulate phonemes to: blend them together to form words, identify individual sounds in words, omit or delete sounds from words to develop new words, substitute one sound in a word for another sound to form new words, and perform combinations of these factors for purposes of rhyming and reading words based on word families.

All of these processes involve auditory phonemic awareness skills, and they are underlying skills necessary for success in reading and spelling. People with normal phonemic awareness skills do these processes mentally. They then learn to overlay onto these mental processes the symbols we call letters and to which we have arbitrarily assigned specific phonemes. However, a child with poor auditory phonemic awareness may not have the internal mental manipulation skills to learn the sound-to-symbol associations needed to lead to the final process called reading decoding and phonics. I was one of those children lacking auditory phonemic awareness skills.

In the era when I was in school, educators did not really understand the need to develop these awareness skills in children prior to teaching them reading. Most children just "cracked the code" automatically, and those who did not were considered slow or even retarded. I remember having no idea of what to do when approaching a new word (i.e., sounding out words). If I could not sight read a word, I would guess or freeze up and not read at all. I had no idea how to use context to figure out words I could not decode. I could only sight read and try to avoid being identified as not being able to read.

This persisted until fifth grade when I was placed in the low functioning academic "track." I do not know exactly how the schools made their choices, but the really slow kids, like me, were in lowest numbered class in a grade. I was placed in the class one step above the lowest, what the kids called the "retarded" class. Looking back, I feel sorry for how we treated the lowest level students, but I wonder if we did it to raise our own self-esteem. Being only one class away from the lowest class made me feel like I was one step above "retarded."

Retarded was not a level, not an IQ, or anything meaningful for me. It meant I was a loser and would never be successful. Now I realize it was my poor reading abilities that kept me in that low functioning class.

Fifth grade was unusual, however because our teacher was a man, when most teachers were female. Even better, he was a recent graduate from college with new and innovative ideas, and one of the best ideas had to do with reading.

Although I was in the fifth grade, I was at a first grade level of reading, but so were most of the other kids in my class. Actually, some were much better readers but were very poor in math, but we were all still in a low functioning class.

My reading group was the lowest in the class. If our reading group were identified by names of birds, we'd have been called the Dodo birds. What really changed my ideas about reading occurred one day when our teacher said we could read comic books. Comics! Wow! Who didn't love comics? You could read the few words and look at the pictures and still get a basic understanding of the story. Comic books! Wow!

We were given a choice of which comic books we wanted to read: Superman, Green Lantern (my favorite) or Batman. All the super heroes you could imagine. So, we started with the super hero of super heroes, Superman.

There was just one catch. We had to read all the words from cover to cover. Who cared if we had to read all the words? We were reading comic books!

Of course, there were many words we could not read, but the teacher used them to teach us how to attack these words. We all learned to read and in a short period of time, we were reading with little or no help from the teacher. We also discussed the stories, wrote reviews for other students indicating which were the best and the worst comic books with support for our reasons. We also summarized the stories, identified characters, heroes and villains, and where and when they took place. Sounds like our teacher "tricked" us into writing book reports without our being defensive. And the best part was that other students in our class wanted to know about our reviews so they could decide whether or not to purchase the comic books next time they went to the store.

One day our teacher suggested that we read the Sunday newspaper for our weekend assignment. The newspaper? Never! I had just learned to read comic books, how could I ever read something with few pictures and so many words. But, it was our assignment, and we had to do it.

That Sunday, my father was very impressed when I asked to read the paper after he finished it. When I opened the paper, to my surprise I discovered the comics section!

I started with Dick Tracy and Dondi immediately, and realized, I was really reading a newspaper. On Monday, the teacher asked us to tell about what we had read. In discussing the sections of the newspaper we all read, I learned that everyone was reading the comics. I realized that many of them were continuous stories that I wanted to read about the following weekend. From then on, we discussed the comics we had read every weekend. That was it! I was hooked on comics, not hooked on phonics, but, I was reading.

That year I also learned how to read the classics. The teacher assigned the entire class to read Tom Sawyer and Huckleberry Finn. My reading group was given the book in a format called "Classics Illustrated." We read the classics illustrated version and were able to participate in class discussions. We all learned and wow, did I feel smart!

I could actually discuss a book with the top readers in my class. I learned that there were pieces of the story missing from what I read, so I became motivated to read the actual book, and I did.

So, as you can see, there are many ways to approach the task of reading, and it does not always have to be the traditional way. For some children, we first need to get them "turned on" to reading before they will be open and ready to want to learn to read. In my case, reading was the last thing I wanted to do, but my fifth grade teacher not only boosted my confidence, inflated my self-esteem, made me feel successful, but he made reading fun. He knew that I would like to read and comprehend comic books, which eventually taught me how to read.

A second lesson to learn is the challenge. That teacher challenged us to read every single word in the comic book. When I discovered what I had been missing by not reading the entire book, I wanted to read all the words all the time. So, it is important to challenge students in a positive manner.

A third lesson relates to thinking outside the box. All too often teachers and school personnel get caught up in a reading series or method and do not look to the individual students and their individual learning styles and needs. My fifth grade teacher realized that he had turned our reading group on to comic books, so he used that as a way to get us to write book reports, read a newspaper, and be introduced to classic literature. This led us to read the books after we had read the Classics Illustrated versions.

It is also important to note that as my reading group read comics, we came to words we could not read or decode. It was then that we learned phonics and word attack skills. The teacher picked out difficult words and had us read them in word lists then read the same words in the entire text. Motivation, challenge, positive rewards, increased self-esteem, using tools that work, and focusing on the individual's interests were some of the keys I learned in fifth grade.

Yet, reading is still a challenge for me. Because of my interests and eventual desire to complete a graduate and post-graduate program, I found myself reading everything I could on the topics related to my academic studies. I even read the dedications and forwards as well as the footnotes. However, when it came to reading non-fiction, I found my reading to be slow and not very fluent. Thus, I did not enjoy reading for pleasure. Then I discovered books on tape which compensates for what has become a life-long disability for me. For technical reading, I read text. For some pleasure reading, I read the book. For most of my pleasure reading, I "read" audio recorded books. I read many, many technical articles and books, especially on subjects related to APD. And I thank my fifth grade teacher for showing me that I could learn to read.

Aside from reading, I had another problem during my school years. Listening was not easy for me from elementary school through college. It was only in graduate school that I learned how to listen properly. Since then I have learned to be a successful, appropriate listener.

I remember an incident in college that exemplifies how poor listening affected my academic work. During the first year of undergraduate school, I took a world history class taught by a professor who was a straight lecturer and used no visual aides. He expected all his students to read not only the thick textbook for the course, but assigned additional readings in each section of the course. For example, we had to read the entire section on the history of ancient Greece and at the same time, we were assigned a supplemental book about life in one city in ancient Greece. Well, wasn't that the perfect class for a student with auditory based learning problems who also had significant reading difficulties!

As the course progressed, I could not keep up with the reading assignments, so, I read just from the textbook. I also expected that the exams would be based on class lectures and text book readings. Little did I know that the professor would ask questions that could only be answered from the supplemental readings. Additionally, many of the questions on quizzes and exams were based on the professor's point of view provided only during his lectures. I could not take appropriate notes while listening to him lecture. So, I thought I could depend on my memory.

I listened, focused and tried to write down what the teacher was saying. Unfortunately, the result was that my notes ended up missing a great deal of information. I was lost! I could not remember half of what was presented in class. Additionally, my reading was so slow that I started taking short cuts that only included reading headings, captions below pictures, and key words bolded in the textbook. I had no idea what the material was really saying.

Then came the midterm and two essays! These assignments required support from class lectures and readings that included supplemental readings. Students formed study groups, but I felt too embarrassed to join because I thought they would be aware of how very little I knew about the course. I was back to that "stupid" kid again. I decided to depend on studying whatever I had from my class notes and my readings.

I had no idea of how to answer many of the questions on the midterm. I eventually wound up with an "F" on the midterm and an "F" on the final. But, there was a third grading option, a course paper. I chose a topic in which I was interested and spent a great deal of time in research. My paper was returned to me without a grade but with a note from the teacher that read, "Please see me." I met with the professor and he questioned me about the paper. Looking back, I believe he suspected plagiarism and I could not blame him since I got a B for the paper. He said that the oral defense of my paper was excellent and demonstrated my complete knowledge of the subject. However, since the "F's" outweighed the "B," I failed the course. One of the last things the professor said was that I should consider going to my advisor and taking the course over because if I got more than a "C" it would wipe off the "F" and my record would not be damaged.

I did what he said, but not because it was his advice. I felt humiliated by him and by the course. However, my advisor made the same suggestion, and I trusted him. Also, I had met a girl in college who was taking World History I, the course I had just failed. I told her I was registering for the course, and she said we should take the same section. That was just what I needed, encouragement from someone I want to have as a classmate. Additionally, she said that we could form a study group, which was a very attractive idea.

One of the first things she noticed was how slowly I took notes, so she suggested meeting to compare notes and said I could use her notes to fill in anything I had missed. Essentially, she became my note taker. I was so relieved to know that she was willing to meet with me on a continuous basis. From that time on, we had formed a friendship, not a bad thing for a young college co-ed.

This was only one aspect of my success in this class. The second was the professor and her teaching style. In contrast to the previous professor who only lectured, this professor showed videos, used a lot of visuals, and focused on class discussions rather than pure lecturing.

Additionally, she used only one textbook that happened to be the same one I used for the previous course. Thus, I could now fill in the parts I missed reading before.

She also gave short answer and multiple choice exams with no essays. A term paper was required, but I had no problem with that. My friend and I chose topics that were related so we could do our research together. Plus, it was a topic more related to the final parts of the course, so I was more prepared for the final exam.

Was I surprised! I got an "A" in my final paper and all of my exams giving me a course grade of "A." My advisor was very pleased that I had taken his advice.

So, what lessons are learned from these experiences?

1. Having taken the class the first time, I got an overview of the topic, then taking it the second time, I performed better because I had been "pre-taught" the material when I took the second class.

2. In the second class, some of the names, places, and dates were familiar to me because I remembered them from the first class. Thus, one of the successful strategies for students, even older students, with auditory-based learning problems is pre-teaching. This is a strategy that presents the new vocabulary, underlying concepts, new or unusual uses of language, and both the written and verbal forms of words to the student so that he/she will be better able to catch this information when presented in class.

3. Through the study group, information was reviewed, missing pieces filled-in, and understanding verified. People with auditory-based learning problems should do a review after the lesson to insure what was presented was truly understood and completely processed.

4. Auditory-based learning problems can persist into college and into adulthood. Yet, learning can be successful even if it heavily depends on auditory input through the use of accommodations such as pre-teaching, clarification, verification, and review.

5. Modifications in testing made for a more successful outcome in the second class. The teacher placed less emphasis on essays, and allowed for more multiple choice and fill-in answers. The written work was assessed via class projects and papers. Therefore, all aspects of performance were still assessed, but in a manner that was more conducive to the learning style and needs of a student with an auditory-based learning disability.

These experiences are mere examples of many experiences I have had throughout my life in which my auditory-based learning disability has caused me to have problems or led to the need for accommodations, especially when it came to education. Yet, in spite of my learning problems, I was able to go on to obtain a post-graduate, doctorate and even continuing education beyond my doctorate.

Thus, people with auditory-based learning disabilities can overcome their problems with early intervention and learning appropriate accommodations that they may need for their entire lives. As a child, early intervention was not available since auditory-based learning problems were neither understood nor recognized. But, today we have the ability to recognize these problems and help children with such difficulties to succeed. Additionally, we now have better methods to identify these problems early and then provide accommodations and remediation strategies.

An underlying theme of my experiences has been the need to develop self-confidence so that difficult learning situations can be overcome. Also, it was necessary for me to have a strong sense of self-esteem. Another important lesson is the importance of the teacher's learning style and his/her approach to teaching and testing. My fifth grade teacher knew just how to "turn on" the non-readers and make us want to read. My second college history teacher had the right teaching style to make me love history and perform well in her class.

My fifth grade teacher and college professor made me feel that I was successful, and because I felt successful, I did not allow my auditory based learning problems to stand in my way of success. In the process, I found my personal interest in the field of auditory information processing disorders. What I went through, many others have gone through and still do, and I understand their struggles.

We, as a society, can all understand their struggles if we step back and think of what it would be like to try to understand someone talking to us at about 250 words per minute or speaking in a foreign language that is only slightly familiar to us. Today we can recognize these disabilities and help people with auditory processing problems (APD) overcome their deficits and become the best they are meant to be.

What is surprising to many may be that although I was *not* a good writer; through hard work and the help from a couple of wonderful, dedicated teachers, I learned to become a very proficient writer and a published author. I now have a love of history and have even become a published historian in the field of APD (see Lucker, 2007b).

Chapter Four

Harvey Edell's Life with an Auditory Learning Disability

by Harvey Edell

My name is Harvey Edell. At 68, I learned that I had an Auditory Processing Disorder or APD.

For the first time in my life, I realized that my learning problem had a name. Finally, I didn't feel stupid. I realize that this may sound strange coming from a college graduate, a top craftsman in the lithographic industry, an artist, teacher and a tutor, but it's true! A quick overview of this disorder is that although I hear what is said, my mind does not decipher all the information. Learning in a school situation had been exceedingly frustrating. My daughter, Loraine, realized that she has this problem as well. *(see Loraine's story, chapter five),* and how she felt all her life fighting her frustrations, and how her son, Andrew *(see Andrew's story, chapter 6),* by receiving the appropriate help, was able to overcome his feelings of frustration and become a very good student.

My daughter had taken the tests that confirmed that she had APD. She said, "Dad, I'm afraid to take the tests," she confided in me one day. "If I don't have this disability then maybe I am stupid."

My daughter went through very rigorous schooling maintaining an A minus average and is now a successful psychologist. You can imagine how very proud I am of her. From the description of the problems she faced in her life because of her APD and the mutual feelings we shared about my possible auditory disability, we decided that I should be tested as well. I was probably more frightened of the results than I let on. I wondered what would happen if I were not found to have an auditory processing problem!

Can you picture being told that your learning problems were because you were stupid? I took the tests and was diagnosed with APD. I felt relieved to discover that my learning disability was due to a legitimate disorder.

To get a better understanding of how APD has affected my life, I would like to tell you a bit of my personal history. I was born in Williamsburg, an old section of Brooklyn, nearly seven decades ago. My earliest memory of first grade was that I found the games that the children played, such as "Ring-Around-the-Rosie" difficult. I did not understand why I couldn't follow the directions that other children found easy to follow.

In early elementary grades, I was always behind in workbook assignments. I remember my first grade teacher telling my mother I was very shy and didn't mingle with the other children. I am sure this was due to my speech and listening difficulties. I had trouble pronouncing the sounds "s" and "sh." For example, from the first to the fourth grades, I would say "sheet" instead of "seat." I was very fearful the children would make fun of me. Imagine what I said for the word "sit?" When I was in the fourth grade, the school provided me with speech therapy in which I used a mirror to try to correct my speech. It did not help.

I did not understand why I was always punished in school. I had to either stand or sit in the corner with my back to the class. In retrospect I realized that I didn't listen to the teacher, therefore I didn't do as I was told.

I now realize that because of APD, it was likely that I wasn't aware of what I was doing wrong. Had I been in the school system today, I would probably have been sent to the school psychologist for an evaluation, with perhaps further testing that would identify the problem as APD.

Today, if parents are made aware of these problems, their children can get outside help from specialists in auditory based learning disabilities. Today, children do not have to suffer with feelings of humiliation and inadequacy.

Another problem area for me in elementary school was math.

The teachers never gave individual help to me in math. My parents were unable to help because they did not understand what it took to make me understand math. Geography was extremely difficult as well, for example we had to know the products of each country. I found that memorizing rote facts was almost impossible. The rote memorization included spelling words which I consistently failed to spell correctly. I also couldn't memorize the multiplication tables.

My memory problems even affected me in music. Children were supposed to know many songs, which included, "My Country 'tis of Thee," "Halls of Montezuma." I pretended that I knew the words by mouthing the words as others articulated them. When it came to history, which I always loved, again I felt like I hit a brick wall. Names and dates, which I could not memorize, were considered of prime importance, so I did poorly in a subject I truly loved.

If my teachers were able to recognize my strengths, instead of trying to fit my skills into their preconceived notions of how to learn, they could have helped me to be a better student. For example, when I didn't obey their rules they should have found out why, instead of making me feel like a failure.

For example, a math teacher I had in eighth grade, taught very well. I was probably the best algebra student in her class; however, I was unable to follow her directions turning the paper over from left to right. Whatever problems I did on the other side of the page were marked wrong. Again, I was being penalized for my disability. Had she been aware that I had an Auditory Processing Disorder she may have acted differently.

Nobody understood or recognized APD disorders in 1947. Children have a much better chance at learning today, but parents must be vigilant in helping them. Teachers must be made aware of student's strengths, weaknesses and learning disabilities.

My brother Charles gave me a Grimm's fairytale book when I was about eight. I struggled to read it as my reading level was below what it should have been. Charles was over anxious about my reading difficulties. Nobody helped me and I felt very frustrated. Eventually I discovered a way to read better. Comic books were interesting and helped me to both enjoy the reading process and to be a better reader. Of course adults did not think comic books had any redeeming value but I continued to read them throughout college. It even seemed strange that I would read about philosophy or science while I was still reading comics. Now the comic books have been replaced with novels and books on science, history, and education that deal with children with learning disabilities.

Right up through college, my grades were mostly poor on papers that I wrote. One exception in high school was an English teacher who gave me two grades: I got a "D" for spelling and grammar and an "A" for content. In college, an English instructor said my oral presentations were far better than anything that I wrote.

Throughout school I was also told that my handwriting was terrible. Adding that to my poor spelling and grammar, I could understand why my teachers did not think well of my academic abilities. Today people have computers and spell checkers. I was so afraid of making mistakes, that it took tremendous effort on my part to write a single sentence, let alone a paragraph or an entire essay assignment. I scrutinized each word so much that I would forget the topic that I was writing about.

I now tutor children from first grade through junior high school. When I teach them writing I tell them not to worry about spelling or grammar. After their first draft, I tell them to go over the paper again and make any necessary corrections, and that I will explain any grammar or spelling errors.

I also praise them for their effort and ideas and explain that they will get better with practice. Thus, I start to build their self-confidence. I also do not hide the fact that I am poor in spelling and that I put a lot of effort in learning the principles of grammar. I have had many children not only improve in their writing, but also earn higher grades. I wish somebody had helped me in this manner many years ago.

When I help children with math, I teach many of the strategies I use. I still have trouble with math. For example, I have difficulties with the multiplication tables and so-called simple problem solving at fourth and fifth grade levels. I show the children that if you can't remember all the multiplication tables, there are alternative ways to quickly obtain the correct answers. I used these alternative methods (i.e., strategies) to cope with my problem. I do stress that they try to learn the multiplication tables as it will make their lives much easier. I attempt to get them not to fear their problems.

Getting over fearing one's problems is important. Even though I had these difficulties in math, I got through calculus because I did not allow my fears to overcome me. When I couldn't remember a solution, I devised another method to use instead. Memorization was not only a problem in math, but it affected other subjects as well.

One of the greatest problems throughout my schooling is that I was made to feel inferior and stupid. I could analyze and understand information much better than most people, but I was forced to listen and memorize, my two weakest areas.

Another problem I have had was answering questions on tests. In college, one of my classes was classical mythology. I understood the work very well but was unable to get a good grade because I couldn't answer written questions on the test properly. The teacher gave me a "C" because instead of just answering the questions, which seemed too simple to me, I gave detailed explanations that went beyond the required answer. I never did comprehend the actual limitations of the questions.

Now when I tutor children, I emphasize that they must answer only what the question asks and not give more or less information. Sometimes questions are not used to find the student's comprehension of a subject but to identify how well the student processes and answers questions. The grade is given based on their processing abilities. Unfortunately, education has not progressed very much in the last 50 years. I went to school approximately 50 years ago.

One of my intuitive abilities to succeed was being sensitive to the teacher's voice inflection, body language, and my general understanding of the subject matter. As I was capable of synthesizing these abilities, I labeled this as an intuitive intelligence. This allowed me to know what questions a teacher might ask. At first I thought this ability was supernatural and deliberately did not study no matter how many times I was proven correct I refused to study the questions I predicted would be asked. I did tell my friends what questions would be on a test, and they studied them and did very well.

I was also able to use this gift I call intuition when playing cards. I would know when to go for an inside straight in rummy or win at poker or blackjack. It was like a sixth sense. Being intuitive to a large degree is frightening because, until recently, it was not considered to be an intelligence. Professor Howard Gardner of Harvard is a psychologist and educator and an author of many books dealing with different intelligence.

Some of these include the capacity for language, mathematical reasoning, and interpersonal skills such as relating to others. A more complex interpersonal skill is that of people being able to understand the intentions of others. Those exhibiting this intelligence include religious and political leaders, teachers, therapists and counselors. I believe that intuitiveness is one manifestation of the interpersonal intelligence (Chapman, 1993). I could have used this intelligence to a much greater degree if I were able to express my fears about it. Now I realize that it was a type of intelligence and not mystical. The study of different intelligences should not stop. Even though it is just as important to be aware of different abilities, teaching about them should be equally important.

Another activity at which I excelled was playing chess. My oldest brother, Walter, gave me a chess set when I was about eight years old. I learned the basic moves and started to play with a friend. I enjoyed the game and played it on and off for many years. When I was in college, I beat a friend of mine who was on the school chess team. Unfortunately, I never wanted to learn the necessary moves that would have made me a better player because it was more fun thinking of my own moves. I know now that memorizing those complex moves would have been difficult and burdensome.

Teaching people to their strengths is very important. If I can digress for a moment to tell you a story about how I was taught to fire a rifle in the US Army, this will demonstrate the point regarding the importance of teaching people to their specific strengths. Recruits in basic training were treated as if they were all right-handed with the same length arms. I was able to score well at the firing range since I am right handed and my arm length is almost average. When I finished basic training, after making any adjustments I deemed necessary, I seldom missed the bull's eye. The lefties or those with very short or long arms had a much more difficult time learning to fire a rifle the army way. Now, common sense tells you that the army way was absurd.

The controversy of teaching reading by whole words or phonics seems to me to be just as foolish. I believe in teaching to the child's strengths and needs, whether it is whole word or phonetics, not arbitrarily choosing one method to fit all children. I hope that more schools would take this same approach and vary their teaching to meet each individual child's strengths and needs.

The most common methods for teaching are only based on reaching the majority of the school population. Those who are unable to learn with the approved ways are given labels: ADD, hyperactive, disruptive, slow, incorrigible, stupid, etc... Reading was taught almost exclusively by phonics when I attended school. This was the worst way to teach me to read. I needed more whole word strategies.

When I tutor children with reading decoding problems, I start them with whole words and linguistics. For me, linguistics involves word parts or word families such as, 'ing,' 'at,' etc... When the children become confident in their reading, I then introduce phonics. When I was taught to sound out words, phonics, I was being taught to my weaknesses. I was a student who learned best by starting with the whole, then breaking it down into parts, and I had APD. It is easy to say that a child doesn't listen, can't catch on to the simplest instructions and just plain difficult to teach. Well, I must admit that my teachers were correct in their evaluation of me based on the methods they used in teaching me.

As far as I am concerned, a large portion of the school population has a learning disability. Don't worry. Most of these problems are normal variations to learning. For instance, there are those who learn analytically, which is the way most students are taught. They mostly use the left side of their brains. They learn one step at a time until they reach the main conclusion. An example would be the use of phonics to learn how to read or to learn proofs in geometry to solve a problem. Accountants might be an example of analytical people.

Those who use the right sides of their brains are predominantly more intuitive. They want to see the whole and then break it down into its parts. Examples would be to learn a word in reading and then break it down into syllables or phonetic units (i.e., individual speech sounds). In geometry, they would first get the solution to the problem and then figure out the proofs. Artists and musicians are good examples of people who might predominantly use the right sides of their brains.

Then there are those who learn best visually while others learn best with their auditory sense. Still others are tactile learners who use the sense of touch. Typists and sculptors might fall into that group. Still others, like those who excel in sports, learn kinesthetically or by movement.

The above examples of the way people learn lets you know that it is not an easy task to teach a class of students. The teacher has to recognize the different learning styles of their students as well as dealing with those students who have learning disabilities and learning problems such as ADD, ADHD, and APD.

My style of learning, along with APD, created learning difficulties for me later in life. This was due to my learning disability in processing oral information as presented by a teacher, or later in life by a supervisor. For me, learning using a whole to part method or using my main intuitive strength, has led to the sharpening of my abilities. This has helped me overcome many of the auditory processing problems. I learned that with very few cues, I was able to understand information that was spoken to me.

I developed coping mechanisms toward the end of college that worked. I always asked questions of my teachers for clarification. I rephrased the original question to be sure that I understood it. When I understood the question, I found it easier to complete the assignment correctly.

When a teacher fails to reach a student and blames the student for not learning, the student may feel like a failure. That was how I felt, and many children may feel the same way in that situation.

Success breeds success and failure breeds more failure. The attitude of the teacher influences the climate of the session. If the tutor or teacher creates a tense atmosphere, a number of children will find it difficult to learn. I found that having fun with my students while teaching them is beneficial during my tutoring sessions. Teachers who display anger and resentment towards children do not obtain their children's best efforts. How I wish that my early grade teachers had displayed concern for me rather than berating and insulting me. This reminds me of the song "Just a spoonful of sugar helps the medicine go down" from the movie Mary Poppins (Walsh 1964)."

Another strategy I learned and still use is when I am thinking of something or explaining something. What I do is go very quickly over the words in my mind and sometimes rephrase them. I stimulate my mind whether by looking at artwork to help me get a subject for a painting or reading books on learning disabilities to get ideas to help the children I tutor. I also tend to do simple math problems in my head. These methods help me to concentrate and block out distractions such as the noise around me.

Another good training method to help people with auditory processing problems is listening to audio stories. Radio played a large role in my entertainment as I grew up. The programs on radio were similar to present-day TV shows, but there was no picture screen. You had to mentally visualize, that is make the pictures in your mind. I believe this was very good training to help people with auditory processing problems. I also liked when an adult read to me when I was small. I still remember a story about a hippopotamus that somebody read to me while I had the mumps. This was when I was five or six years old and not going to school yet. Again, as the adult would read, I would visualize.

My interests in learning may have been a reason that, in the late nineteen sixties, I decided to change occupations and become a teacher. I first took the oral exams and was told that I did very well. The person evaluating me said that my ideas on education were very advanced and asked if I think I could get along with other teachers. I had only one education course, so the ideas I elaborated on were all mine. Then the written test came. I practiced my writing as much as possible, but to no avail. I had two words spelled wrong beyond what they allowed. I failed. This experience occurred in 1968. It discouraged me from ever taking the test to become a teacher again.

One problem I had growing up was that loud and reverberant noises drove me crazy. The echoes at the swimming pool at the YMHA hurt my ears. When I went into the subway with my mother to visit my aunt, again the noise caused me pain. When my brother played the drums, I would cover my ears and hide under the bed. This sensitivity to sound occurred at an early age probably between the ages of five and ten. Even loud sounds at the movies bothered me. The thought of loud noises was enough to put me into a frenzy. Once my APD was found, I understood that problems with noise tolerance may be related to auditory processing sensitivity deficits.

Another problem area that may have been related to my auditory processing deficits was related to playing group sports. During the years from my childhood through my early teens, I did poorly in group sports. Nobody wanted me on his/her team. I was very good at handball during this time. I was also good at three or four person sports like touch football or three-man basketball. I was able to hit the ball well in softball, but I was not a good team player or fielder. Teams consisted of many players increasing the noise level and my distractibility making it difficult for me to concentrate and communicate with my team members. All the noise and the way teammates would try to yell out would confuse me or bother my hearing.

Through the years I have had difficulty following directions. This was not only a problem following orally presented instructions, but a problem with directionality. For example, when I rode a bicycle for Western Union I never knew whether to make a left or right turn. Later, when I was driving a car I had the same problem. Also, if I were given directions that involved a few turns, my mind would go blank. I solved this problem in two ways. First, I would write the directions down with diagrams. Then, I would ask a few more people as I progressed on the trip. Once portable phones were available, I find I use my cell phone to help me. Many times I enlist the help of a person in a car or I read a map on which I have placed arrows to help me navigate.

Not only did I depend on other adults to help me navigate, but I relied on children as well. For example, my son, when he was three years old, would help me with directions. One time, I was riding in the country where I had a vacation home and was going someplace at night and made the wrong turn even though I'd made the correct one many times during daylight hours. My three year old son, sitting in the back seat, said "Daddy you made the wrong turn." Because of my problem with directions I become very nervous before going on car trips. But, I learned that there are ways I can make it easier for me.

Following directions leaves me feeling nervous so I avoid directions whenever possible such as instructions for assembling a television stand. I find oral and written instructions difficult to follow. I feel that this condition is part of my APD problems. I never had much confidence in myself when it came to doing mechanical projects. My brother Stan always believed in my abilities while my father did not. Stan's belief in me helped me gain confidence in myself. It seems that many people had confidence in my abilities and many still do. This has helped me to have confidence in myself and my own abilities and has encouraged me to build things like the TV stand.

Other people having confidence in me have helped me in other areas in which I have had problems. For example, writing and editing have always been difficult for me. Yet, once a friend of mine named Jack, a psychiatrist, asked another friend of ours, Phil, who was a rabbi and going for a doctorate in ancient history, to give me an editorial that he was writing for the Jewish Press so that I could make comments on the article. We were at the beach when I read the editorial. I told Phil, who wrote it, that I thought it was terrible. I then proceeded to outline in detail how I thought the topic should be handled. He listened to me but didn't comment on my critique. Therefore, I wondered whether he really felt my critique was valid. Two months later while we were all at a show, Phil handed me the Jewish press with his article published in it. I was flabbergasted that

he listened to me and rewrote the entire editorial using all of my recommendations. I had read many books on ancient Jewish history and
had taken a few Jewish philosophy courses at a yeshiva. I was able
to use this knowledge to give a worthwhile criticism of Phil's article.
But, I was pleased that my friend, Phil, would take my editorial criti-
cisms to heart and use what I had suggested.

It seems that even with knowledge that made me a good critic,
my lack of self-confidence did not allow me to see my worth. When
I was in the printing field people listened and used my suggestions. I
felt that maybe I wasn't qualified to give this advice. I felt like I was
a failure most of the time I was in school, whether it was elementary
school or college. Even when I was doing very well in the printing
industry I felt that I should not have been in that profession. I just
never lived up to my expectations of myself. The one big exception is
my tutoring. I feel now that I am doing something useful. I find both
the children and their parents seek out and take my advice. This has
led me to feel more confident in myself and my abilities.

I know that I am capable and have been correct in most of my
assessments of myself. However, this does not diminish my feelings
of inadequacy. I never stopped trying to do better because I want
to deserve the acclamations I receive. I do not know whether I will
have full confidence in my past, present, and future abilities so in the
meantime I will try harder and harder to be the best I can.

One of my strengths is the ability to ask the right questions that
lead people to the right answers. For example, after graduating college I went into the printing business. My job was to take the original artist's work and redo it for printing. I always asked questions
when I was given a job. I made sure I understood what I was to do.
Many times my questions forced the foreman to get further information from the boss or client. I also had a habit of analyzing the job
and giving the client, foreman, or boss my feelings about how the job
could be improved, or what parts of the job could not be done. There
were many ways to handle a job. Each complicated job may have had
a dozen or more solutions. The more complicated the job the better I
liked it.

My desire to do complicated jobs was also recognized by others. One of my co-workers told the supervisor that he shouldn't give me anything simple because I would make mistakes. He was right. My mind would wander and I would make mistakes. However, when I was given a complex job, I was forced to concentrate to my fullest abilities I tended to ignore the distractions around me such as people talking, the radio playing, or somebody trying to have a conversation with me.

One other strength I have had growing up is doing artwork. My trade was very demanding on my artistic abilities. Thus, I was able to excel at it. When I was in school, I continually used my artistic talents. My notebook in junior high school science was full of relevant sketches. When I was in college taking Art History, I drew the slides that were shown in my notebook. However, I never got extra credit for these efforts.

Although I grew up thinking myself stupid, I no longer think of myself as being stupid. I am a good teacher. I have helped dozens of children and their families by not only giving the children the knowledge to succeed in school, but also by giving them the confidence they need to succeed. I minimize their disabilities while helping them overcome the areas of learning that they find so overwhelming and difficult. I use their strengths to make them feel good about themselves and be willing to learn to do work that they thought they could never do.

Overcoming my own learning problems and calling upon my intuitive abilities has allowed me to help my students. My intuitiveness and empathy in teaching are natural tools that I forged while I worked through my disability. I am who I am because, not in spite of, my auditory processing disabilities.

Many famous people had learning problems. Albert Einstein was dyslexic, but as everyone knows this disability did not stop him from changing the way we view the universe. George S. Patton was a late reader who did poorly in spelling and grammar but became one of our best generals. William Butler Yeats was also a late reader who had atrocious handwriting and never learned to spell. I read his poems in college. Having problems with reading, spelling, and grammar did not stop these people from being good at their occupations. Some even excelled and became the best in their fields.

Helping children succeed is one of the most important goals in education. Yet, there is a tendency for people to fit children with learning problems into categories such as AD/HD, APD, etc. This serves a purpose when a teacher or parent can use these categories to help a child succeed. Unfortunately, when the student has a label attached to his learning abilities, he may feel a stigma being learning disabled. The teacher may not look any further into the child's abilities but, instead, be satisfied with the child's limitations because of the classification. Children as well as adults, however, do not necessarily fall into any preconceived category. I would prefer teachers and parents see the child as a whole human being. Children have many more strengths than weaknesses. And these strengths can be used to teach them and help them succeed.

In my attempts to better understand learning and success, I took a psychology course in college. This was in the late fifties. I asked the instructor why the various psychologists had to be for one or another approach to psychology. Some were Freudian while others followed the Youngian approach. Even then I couldn't understand why different and maybe opposing ideologies could not be integrated to help a person. I did not receive an answer. Many years later I learned that the most successful therapists actually use a combination of the leading methods to better treat their patients.

This has influenced me in my tutoring as well. In teaching a child to read I found the controversy of phonics versus whole word learning absurd. Both are good for different children at different times in their lives. I went to an elementary school to speak with a first grade teacher once about a student with whom I was tutoring who could not learn phonics at that time. She listened to me and then proceeded to send notes home to the parents about his inability to use phonics. I felt that he was a very bright child and started him reading an interesting book when I was tutoring him. The stories gradually increased in difficulty and had beautiful pictures accompanying the stories. I played games with this boy using the words in the story.

His memory was superb. He could look at a five-letter word for a few seconds and spell it to me either forwards or backwards. This memory trick helped to increase his confidence in himself. One day, I came over to tutor the child and he told me that he read a story to the teacher. I knew that this was impossible for him to do, and I scolded him about lying to the teacher. He memorized the story, but was unable to read the words. I confronted the child, and he smiled and agreed not to lie again. He was very bright and had a photographic memory.

The point I am making is that children like this boy left to their own devices are capable of going through school without ever learning to read. Therefore, I ask that parents and teachers be careful how you judge children. The boy I just discussed is now in eighth grade and in honors classes. He needed someone to motivate him and help him to learn to read and not depend on "tricks" to make people think he knew how to read.

Again, if I may digress, I would like to recount some of my memories of my daughter Loraine's problems and strengths as a child. The reader can learn more about her in the chapter she wrote and is part of this book *(chapter 5)*. When Loraine was between two and three years of age, she was not yet able to talk, but her pantomime was so understandable that her young friends, who were a year older than she was, understood her and followed her lead. Whatever Loraine decided they should do, they followed and did the same, like playing games or coloring with crayons. Her leadership abilities were evident even at that young age.

Loraine was six years old when my daughter Sherri, her sister, was born. Loraine helped set up her room knowing she was to share it with her sister. She went over her toys and helped choose which should go to the basement and then helped me bring them downstairs. Without any exaggeration, her help was indispensable to me.

When Loraine finished kindergarten, her teacher recommended that we should take her for speech therapy. Her speech was not understandable. We took her to Brooklyn College in New York City for a speech evaluation and then for speech therapy. We were told that her speech had to be slowed down as she was thinking faster than she could talk. We were also told that her vocabulary and intelligence were above her age level. I do not know what tests were used nor what her IQ level was. But, we accepted that our daughter had a speech problem.

In addition to going to school, Loraine started Hebrew School, an after-school program. When I observed her in class, she did not seem to me to be paying attention. I spoke to her teacher to find out how she was doing. I was told that my daughter outperformed most of the children in her class in arts and crafts. So, I thought maybe it would be a good idea for her to pursue some special work in art.

My daughter wanted to learn how to draw so I hired somebody to teach her. This was a big mistake. She did not like this teacher and was turned off to art because of this teacher. Before taking these lessons, Loraine did a painting that I thought was beautiful and I hung it up. When she was in junior high school she won first prize in a poster contest for which she made a collage on the topic of not smoking.

Though she never tried painting or drawing again, she used her creative talents in photography. Looking back, I realize that her confidence in her abilities was so low that if she thought she would fail at something, she would rather not try again. Thus, she never went far in the creative arts.

When Loraine was in the lower elementary grades, I became concerned that she was first placed into an advanced class and the following year put into a slow class. I saw the principal and asked her why a child could be bright one term and dumb the next. I did not get a satisfactory answer so I told the principal that my daughter was not a yo-yo. The next year I enrolled her in a Jewish day school, a yeshiva where she performed well and succeeded in school.

Helping children with auditory processing problems and learning disabilities is critical. Looking over my life from the perspective of my learning disability, I can see many positive ways it could have been enhanced based on the present knowledge I now have that I have an auditory processing disability. This knowledge, combined with knowing how to teach children having differing learning styles, could have helped me succeed. My early elementary school years could have left me with positive feelings about my learning had assistance been provided to me. After tutoring many children and having worked in the school system, I realize that the knowledge that is available to properly teach and improve a child's perception of himself may not be enough. The classrooms are crowded and the teachers find it difficult to give a child with learning disabilities the extra attention he/she needs while teaching the rest of the class. We need to provide the support these children need as well as the teacher's need to provide appropriate education for children with auditory processing problems.

Presenting these experiences with my disability and how I coped with them has allowed me to show you how difficult it is to live with auditory based learning disabilities when there is no help available. Today we understand that a person can overcome a learning disability such as APD. Today there is help, but unfortunately many school systems seem unable to deal with the problems without outside help. Therefore, parents must help their children. If you notice that your child is failing at school or losing self-confidence, it is up to you to get help for him/her. I have had success in tutoring children with many learning problems, and I know that there are many caring tutors available. When it comes to an auditory-based, learning disability, such as APD, I would recommend a speech and language pathologist that deals specifically with such problems for providing some of the remedial help. Additionally, an audiologist who specializes in this area should provide an appropriate assessment of the APD problems. It must be noted that APD is not a typical area in which audiologists have knowledge and experience, especially related to how such learning problems affect a child's education and what recommendations can be provided to treat such problems. My grandson's account of the help he has had and how this help translated into higher grades and increased self-confidence should give you hope *(see chapters five and six)*. Every child that I am able to help empowers me as well as the child. So, if I have helped you to see both the problems that a person faces with an auditory-based learning disability and what can be done about it, this writing effort was worth it.

Chapter Five

Loraine Alderman's Struggles with Having an Auditory Processing Disorder

by Loraine Alderman, Psy.D.

My name is Loraine Alderman. I am a wife, mother and a doctor of psychology. It was only recently that I was diagnosed with APD, an Auditory Processing Disorder, although I have lived with it for over forty years. I have accomplished much, in spite of having an APD and never having had any treatment or assistance with this disorder.

I am currently a licensed clinical psychologist and a certified school psychologist. I have published an article in the Omega Journal of Death and Dying and written a column for a community newspaper for two years on various mental health issues. I was also interviewed regarding mental health issues two times by Donna Hanover on "Good Day New York" television. My professional background includes working as a psychologist in an outpatient inner city hospital and as a coordinator for two in-patient psychiatric units in an inner city hospital. For the last five years, I have worked in the school system as a school psychologist. Additionally, I have a private practice in which I see patients for psychotherapy. I also perform evaluations for children trying to get into gifted programs and for children whose parents need to determine if their child has a learning disability.

When I explain to my students and their parents that I have APD, they are usually quite surprised that I have such a problem. The truth is that over the years I have taught myself to mask or compensate for my APD.

My earliest memories regarding any academic difficulties were of going to speech therapy and reading classes. My parents removed me from public school and put me in a private religious school for the fifth and sixth grade. They changed schools because each year the public school wanted to move me from the top class to the bottom and then back to the top class.

At that time, students were tracked based on scores from standardized tests and were put into classes based on these scores. The decisions were based on tests that were given each year, and apparently no one questioned why my performance on these tests varied so much year to year. It was easier to just change my class. When my parents realized what was happening, they decided to send me to a private school, where I was tutored for English and Hebrew.

It was in the fifth grade that I recall being aware of having difficulty learning certain topics. I could not remember the Roman numeral system or understand specific topics in my Hebrew studies. I returned to public school and while in the seventh and eighth grades, academics became painful. I have vivid memories of crying at my desk. No matter how I tried, I could not understand the grammar lessons from my English class.

I also had difficulties socially. Between the tendency to be concrete and having just come out of spending two years in a religious school, I was a prime target for my peers who took full advantage of these inadequacies. Socially and academically, middle school was a miserable experience because I didn't know why I was having such difficulties.

In high school, I felt stupid a good portion of the time because I didn't understand how I could misunderstand the assignment directions so often.

New York State has regents' exams that are given for Algebra, Geometry, Trigonometry, Biology, Chemistry, English and Social Studies, as well as Foreign Languages. Currently the passing grade has been reduced to a score of 55 in the hopes that more students will pass. However, when I attended school 65 was the passing score. With the exception of Algebra, I managed to fail every regent by usually one to three points.

When I started high school, I picked Hebrew as my foreign language hoping that all the years in after school programs and two years in Yeshiva would give me an advantage. Well, it did for the first half of the year, but then I began to have difficulties, so I decided to try Spanish because I had studied it in middle school. It became apparent that as soon as grammar became important, I could no longer tread water in a foreign language class.

When I asked my guidance counselor to take me out of foreign language, he informed me that I would not be able to get a Regent's Diploma if I did not complete a foreign language sequence. I asked him to look over my record because based on my regents scores I was not going to get one anyway. I graduated with a local diploma and decided not to attend college after graduation.

When I returned to college after a few years (I had tried six credits one year after graduating from high school), I went back to my high school to get the necessary information for my application. The secretary asked if I wanted my SAT scores on the application. My response was, "I took them?" The only memories that I have of taking them were vague. The secretary then politely suggested that she did not think that it would be a good idea to put the scores on the application. Apparently they were less than impressive and omitting them would be wiser than letting the college see my scores. When I entered the working world, no matter what type of job I performed, I had difficulty learning paperwork procedures. Around the mid 80's, I was convinced that I had a hearing loss. What else could explain the way I kept missing things that people said? My mother was working in the Speech and Language Department at a nearby hospital, and at my request, she asked an audiologist to give me a hearing test. When the test came back negative, I concluded that if I didn't have a hearing loss I must be stupid after all. How else could I explain all the difficulties that I was experiencing?

I had difficulty with things that my peers found easy, and frequently misunderstood what people told me, especially car directions. I could never remember directions after the first left or right turn. If the person used the terms "South, North, East or West," I had no clue of which way to go.

My husband has tried many times to explain this concept to me, and much to his dismay and frustration, those terms still mean nothing. When I use a map, I turn the map around so that the map is facing the same direction in which I am traveling so I know which way to turn.

During the period in which I had my hearing tested, I was working six days a week in a school supply store. I had always wanted to be a teacher, and coming into contact everyday with teachers reminded me of my earlier career thoughts. I also did not want to be working six days a week, with two weeks vacation when I was in my 60's. So, despite my frustrations and feelings of being stupid, I decided to attempt to go back to school at night for my college degree. I started with one class and added more each semester. At one point, I was taking 13 credits while working 40 to 60 hours a week.

When it came time to hand in papers, I had my husband and friends proof read them for spelling (pre-computer spell-check era) and grammar. I frequently alternated between tenses. I knew that without editing, I would get lower grades. My husband and friends often told me as my writing became more technical, that they had no clue what they were reading, but would try their best to proof them.

One of the most frustrating times in undergraduate school was when I was majoring in Early Childhood Education. The class involved how to teach phonics to young children. This class became my worst nightmare. I could not hear the phonetic differences in many of the letters, nor understand the long and short vowel sounds. I felt like a total idiot.

I switched Early Childhood Education from being my major, to being my minor and made Psychology as my major in the next semester. How could I ever teach children what they needed to learn if I couldn't understand it myself?

As I progressed in my studies, it became apparent that if I wanted to make a good living in the field of psychology, I would have to go for a doctorate degree. Eventually, I graduated from Brooklyn College with a 3.98 Grade Point Average (GPA) in Psychology and a 3.80 overall GPA. My only B in Psychology was in my Statistics class.

You would think that with those grades I would no longer think that I was stupid, but you would be wrong. Although I had worked very hard to obtain those grades, I still felt insecure about my intellectual abilities. Those insecurities were confirmed and nourished by some of the graduate school professors who made me feel like I had three heads the way they responded to my questions. The neurology professor took my show of weakness as an opportunity to humiliate me at every opportunity in front of my classmates. To compound this situation, I found learning the different models of the brain to be as difficult as the times I had tried to learn phonetics and grammar.

Looking back, I find it remarkable that a professor who specialized in identifying learning disabilities never considered that I may have had one. But, I came from a generation in which you were not identified as having a learning problem unless you were a troublemaker.

During my undergraduate and graduate years of school, I often waited until after class or during breaks to ask the teachers questions. My son, Andrew tends to do the same thing. I wish I had thought of this strategy in my earlier years in school.

During my statistics classes, I spent more time with a classmate at her house where she was tutoring me than I did at my own house. No matter how much tutoring I received, I could not understand statistics even if my life depended on it. Fortunately, my professor recognized that something was out of my control and was causing me to have problems in his class, and based my grade primarily on the research half of the class. He seldom penalized me for an inability to understand statistics.

Fortunately, in addition to the professors who made me feel like a bumbling idiot, I had one professor who was great for improving my self-esteem. At the end of my first year in graduate school, when I was almost ready to call it quits, she asked to have a copy of one of my papers that she had liked very much. This professor, was the chairperson of the department at a renowned university, was internationally known, and had published several books and countless journal articles. Her request did wonders for my self-esteem and gave me the courage to continue to try even harder, as if that were possible. I still keep in contact with her. Her continued belief in my ability, encourages me to try things like writing for a community newspaper and a book.

Some interesting aspects of living with APD that I did not go into earlier are things that my son, and I have in common. We both cannot tolerate loud noises or very crowded places. Andrew tends to be more sensitive to noise than I am. However, some noises drive me crazy, especially those to which most people don't give a second thought. For example, if my husband puts the fan in the living room on "high", I cannot eat in the adjoining dining room area because the sound agitates me. At work, I had to ask a colleague to turn off the floor fan because I could not concentrate on writing my reports. No one else in the office had been bothered by the sound of that fan.

I also have a poor conception of time. I wear a watch that I can set for increments of five minutes up to thirty. When I am food shopping or working on a task at work and need to be done by a certain time, I set the watch to beep at ten or fifteen minute intervals. Without setting my watch to beep to keep me aware of the time, food shopping could easily turn from a one-hour to a multiple-hour experience. I also have to set my watch when I leave my office to take care of things around school or I could easily end up back at my office one-hour later instead of fifteen minutes later.

Being a school psychologist, I get to participate in many meetings with parents and their advocates. Besides advocating for the student presented at meetings, I also look for new ideas regarding how to help my son and other children with similar auditory-based learning problems. A few years ago, a parent came to a meeting with a large organized binder that included a section for all past speech and psychological testing that had been done, one section for her child's IEP's (Individualized Educational Plans), and other sections for specific things related to her child. I thought that this was a great idea since Andrew's papers were stuffed into a folder that was bursting at the seams.

Needless to say, I obtained a binder and organized my son's papers. I also tell every parent I meet to get a binder to do the same.

It is much easier to locate things in a binder than to find a folder that may have gotten mixed up in a pile of papers at home. Additionally, when I conduct meetings at my school I offer a note pad and pen to parents. I let them know that they can feel free to call me with any questions about anything.

When my father (Harvey Edell) first suggested writing this book, I have to say that two thoughts ran through my mind. I wondered if my colleagues would look at me differently if I exposed this part of myself? I had worked very hard at obtaining a good reputation and was afraid that I might be viewed differently if I exposed this side of myself.

People with whom I trust and am very close to, have responded in a positive, supportive manner. Yet, this was a big concern of mine as I have learned through years of difficulty in which I have worked hard to compensate for and mask my APD. I have also shared knowledge of my own APD with parents of students who have recently been identified with APD and wonder how their children will succeed in life. This sharing helps alleviate some of their anxieties and concerns. I'm not ashamed of having an APD, however, I often wondered if sharing my experiences with APD would have any negative effects on my professional life.

The second concern I had about writing this book was, how my son would react to sharing his disabilities with the world? I have always respected his privacy and would not share that information to any teachers, coaches, or caretakers without first discussing the matter with him. As I stated, I am not ashamed about sharing my APD and I am also not ashamed of my son's APD, and neither is he. However, I did not want to invade his right to privacy. I can only wonder since I, as a professional, had these fears, how do other parents feel about allowing other people to know about their children's disabilities.

There may be some prejudices and stigmata that go along with APD as well as with other learning disabilities, and most of them stem from people who do not fully understand them. Sometimes children and adults can be extremely cruel.

Growing up, I knew that I had difficulty learning different subjects in school, but I didn't know why. When the audiologist said that my hearing was fine, I just assumed that, at times, I was stupid or a slow learner. It was not until I started to learn about my son's Auditory Processing Disorders that I suspected that I had one too. This was not a disorder that had been covered in any of my undergraduate or graduate classes.

As I started to read the literature about APD I recognized many of the symptoms in myself, but I did not pursue finding out if I had an APD for a few years. I later shared with some people, including my father, that I felt I had a form of what my son had. For the most part, people did not give this much thought however my father did and asked to learn more about APD. A few years ago, I started to have what I refer to as my "mid-life awakening." I had turned 41 and decided that I was no longer going to hold myself back from doing things, and that I wanted to get the most out of life. I spoke with my son's speech-language pathologist about having myself tested for APD. We had formed a bit of a bond and I felt very comfortable discussing this with her. She thought that it would be a great idea, and with her support and encouragement, I decided to have myself tested.

I was very nervous on the day of the assessment and was scared that if the test came back normal, it would confirm that I was either stupid or a very slow learner. After the testing was completed, I thought that the day when I would get the results of the assessment would never arrive. Finally, the appointment to review my test results arrived. As the director of the speech center and I were going into her office, she asked me if her intern could observe the feedback session. I know it sounds silly, but in my head I freaked out a bit. I felt like I was between a rock and a hard place. Having been in the psychology intern position for so many years, I knew that it would be a good learning experience for the intern. On the other hand, if the results were normal, the intern would know that I was stupid after all. I decided to let her observe the session. The director said that the test interpretations and conclusions indicated that I did have an APD and because of that, I couldn't hear phonetic sounds, I sighed with relief.

I immediately called my father and informed him that I wasn't stupid after all. There was a reason for the difficulties that I had experienced. After confirming that I had difficulty processing auditory information, I decided to try some treatment. I figured that I still had many years to live and that maybe it wasn't too late to change. I started therapy with my son's speech-language pathologist. I know that I keep referring to this as speech-language therapy with regard to my son and myself, but it is actually auditory processing training as opposed to what one usually considers speech-language therapy (i.e., difficulty talking or saying words). We worked on computer programs that focused on building recognition of phonetic sounds and my auditory memory. Since most of the clientele consisted of children, the computers, desks and chairs were set up for them.

I must say, it was a humbling experience sitting on a small chair next to children ranging in age from three to eleven. At times, the pathologist would make the task more difficult by covering up part of the computer screen. This caused me to rely on my auditory skills more than my visual skills.

At times, it was extremely aggravating, and I accepted the task as a challenge that would not get the better of me. It also helped that my speech therapist was close to my age and was supportive and encouraging. At times, we were lucky to have the room to ourselves without any kids looking at me and maybe thinking why I was there. When we were alone, the speech-therapist and I would often have to shut down the monitors of the neighboring computers. I found that the screen saver on the other computers near me were distracting, and I was not able to focus.

When the children were in the room, it took a lot of effort for me to not be distracted by them or their computer screens. This may sound more like attention deficit disorder than an Auditory Processing Disorder however, based on my training as a school psychologist, I do not feel that my symptoms meet the diagnostic criteria for such a diagnosis of Attention Deficit Disorder. It's like trying to understand a conversation when you are talking on a cell phone with someone and every few words get dropped. You are paying attention to the speaker at all times, but only catching every other word and trying to make full sentences out of them.

One coping mechanism that I have mainly used over the last ten years is that, when I am at work, I always have pen and paper with me. If I don't write things down immediately, I usually don't remember them by the time that I get back to my office. Therefore, if a teacher catches me in the hallway and asks me to check on a student, or my assistant principal tells me several things she wants done, I can jot the information down very quickly. One of my trademarks at work, so to speak, is that I usually wear an outfit that includes a blazer with pockets for the pen and paper. The few times that I have not worn a blazer to work and found myself two floors away from my office without a pen and paper almost caused me to have a sense of panic.

Since I learned that I have an Auditory Processing Disorder, it has created a unique bond between my son and I. In some way, I feel that having an APD myself, has normalized it a little for my son. For example, when I was working on a particular computer program in my auditory processing training sessions, a program that my son had already completed, he would ask me questions about how I did after my sessions, and he would give gave me suggestions and hints for the next session.

In contrast to helping, there are times when Andrew has difficulty with his math homework and I cannot help because we both interpret the question the same, incorrect way. At times we joke about this dual misinterpretation, and this is especially true when my husband asks us something and we both respond similarly incorrectly. This probably occurred before I was diagnosed with an APD, but at that time we didn't make much of the misinterpretation.

Sometimes Andrew gets frustrated when my father and I try to learn more about APD. While this is something relatively new for me, and very new for my father, my son has been diagnosed and living with an APD and for over eight years. I think he views these learning problems as a minor part of his life. In contrast, my father and I, looking over most of our lives not knowing about APD until now, see it has a major factor. We are trying to understand how our own processing problems have influenced our experiences and influenced who we have become.

Without sounding like an egotist, I know from feedback that I have received from my supervisors and peers, that I am a good clinician. I graduated from undergraduate and graduate schools with decent grade point averages and passed a very difficult licensing exam. A few years ago, at a high school reunion, I caught up with an old friend who was surprised to learn that I didn't go to college right after high school. Her comment to me was, "But I always thought you were so smart." I remember being taken aback by her comment because I never considered myself to be a smart person.

In writing this chapter, I have had to look back at my life and career choices. In one of my recent meetings with the director of the speech center where my son attends sessions, we discussed how I was able to function as a clinician despite my auditory processing difficulties. What we identified, is the fact that when I am in a session with a patient or testing a student it is usually very quiet with little or no distractions.

It seems that my undivided attention is given to the person with whom I am working. I also jot down notes about the session or about the student whom I am testing. This, combined with my increased sensitivity to a person's tone of voice and their facial and body expressions, has helped me compensate in my work as a clinical psychologist.

Even though I have learned to compensate for my APD in my career and in daily life, it would have been much easier if I had been afforded some of the benefits that my son has had, such as a Section 504 plan. At times I wonder whether my level of self-confidence would have been different and whether I would have chosen my current career had I known about why I was having such learning difficulties. Today, we are fortunate to have the ability to identify auditory processing problems and how they affect learning so that a child with an APD does not have to struggle and feel incompetent the way I had to for most of my life.

Chapter Six

Andrew Alderman Growing Up with Auditory Processing Disorder in a Modern World

by Andrew Alderman

When I was in kindergarten, it was difficult for me to learn. I had trouble understanding why I could not pick up things as fast as the other students. I even had problems learning the alphabet, the days of the week, and following directions in class.

I did well at baseball and karate, both of which I started when I was three. I was especially good at karate because it was visual and I mimicked the movements of others, even though it was competitive and a physical challenge. I found baseball difficult when the coaches yelled directions because I had a lot of trouble processing what they were saying while the parents and kids on my team were yelling.

In karate, I had a problem doing some of the moves when the Sensei (teacher) would speak in Japanese, as well as some of the throws such as the positioning of my feet and hands. I had to wait until the teacher demonstrated the throws on me and showed me where to put my feet and hands. I learned the moves quickly when they were demonstrated rather than when they were explained.

I also felt that I wasn't able to do my homework by myself. I knew that something was wrong because the other kids did it by themselves. Often, I didn't know how to do the homework. I was frustrated because I couldn't find the answers ...they were in front of me, but I couldn't find them. I was not confident that I would put the correct answers on my homework sheet or do the tasks correctly. I would try over and over and it would still be wrong. Sometimes I guessed the answers based on what I learned in school that day.

Other times I would not understand the assignment and had to call a friend. Or I would forget the assignment in school and my parents would have to write a note or go to school and get my assignments and materials I needed. This sometimes made my parents and teachers disappointed and angry.

I felt stupid, and that I should be able to do the work by myself. I was disappointed that my parents were frustrated and also that my teachers could not understand why I had so much trouble learning.

I was in the third grade when we moved to East Meadow, Long Island, New York. It was hard for me to make new friends and school subjects became even more difficult. But I was fortunate because I had been tested by a speech-language pathologist. While I was taking speech-language therapy I learned new techniques for doing homework, taking notes from the blackboard, taking tests and listening more carefully. When the school started to provide me with testing accommodations, I felt okay about them, but I also felt embarrassed. Kids would ask me, "Why are you going out of the room for some tests?" I'd try to explain but it was difficult and at one point they thought I was stupid.

I did not always go to another room for all my tests. Sometimes, I took them with the teacher during class like when I took spelling tests. I was confident about taking spelling tests. My parents worked with me with the spelling words, drilling them over and over so that I didn't have to think about them on the day of the test. Since the form of the tests were repetitious, I knew what was to be done. I knew that only the words changed from test to test.

In contrast to spelling tests, taking others like math, and more specifically, word problems and science were more difficult. I had problems with what I was asked to do. I often had to ask to rephrase the question, but I was still confused. I may have known the correct answer but I had trouble matching my knowledge to the way the question was being asked.

I also found I was distracted easily. When I took a test in the classroom, if I heard any hall noises, or teachers talking, or pen tapping, I'd forget my place and have to reread the question again and again. If I sat in front in the class, it helped me pay more attention and be better able to focus, but I wanted the environment to be as quiet as possible when taking tests.

At first, the testing for my disability frightened me and I questioned why it even needed to be done but after a few years of speech therapy, I started to understand my disability how to work around it.

The therapist often included games and visual aids to help me work out my problems. At school, the down side of my problem was that I couldn't sit next to my friends. I had to sit up front next to the teacher. The therapist said this would help me. Another idea that the speech therapist suggested was for me to ask that questions or directions be rephrased. Sometimes teachers wouldn't do this, which made it difficult for me, and I wouldn't say anything to them because I didn't want to be disrespectful.

As I got older, I started to stand up for my accommodations because there were certain tests that I would have failed if I had not insisted on clarification of questions and directions. Some of these tests were high stake tests and could have resulted in me not being promoted to the next grade. As the number of my accommodations increased, I could finally see the results of my studying and my grades improved. Taking tests in a separate room, with no distractions, was much easier than taking them in the classroom. Sometimes this backfired when the proctors would talk and create a distraction.

If teachers gave verbal directions, I often messed up. Sometimes I'd write them down which worked well, but I sometimes I missed something important, that was said as I copied notes in my book.

Before I was provided with accommodations, I used to study a lot for tests and when I got them back, the grades were in the low sixties or seventies. It frustrated me because I didn't know what to do differently to improve my grades. After I received my accommodations, my grades improved, something that I never thought would happen. It was then that I my confidence started to grow and I began to believe in myself.

When I entered middle school, I had some wonderful teachers who understood me very well. One teacher in particular was really nice, and made me feel very comfortable. She taught social studies, and made the class act out as if they were actually living that part of history. We were Cavemen, Aztecs, Egyptians, Medieval Knights and more. Acting out the different parts of history made it easy to remember things.

Not only was she encouraging, but she allowed me to bring in my projects early, and gave me input on how to improve them before handing them in. Since I often misunderstood part of the assignment, this was very helpful. In addition, she taught me what to study for tests and what pages of my notes to read and re-read. My grades were very good in this class, which gave me more confidence to do better in other classes. It helped that the other teachers talked to this social studies teacher and worked out plans to help me. School became fun and rewarding and much less frustrating.

I feel that I succeeded better at sports because it is more visual and I like the competitiveness. There are difficult times when I play sports because there are things that are parts of the game that I don't understand. It is very hard to concentrate when the coach yells directions very fast, and I find it hard to follow at times. It is easier when the coach demonstrates the moves.

It is frustrating when someone gives me verbal directions. For example, when I was the ball boy for the Long Island Lizards (a professional Lacrosse team in my area), one of the players said "Go get my helmet and elbow pads." He said the helmet and pads were in the middle of the locker room near a white T-shirt. It was confusing and frustrating because when I went to the locker room, I found the white shirt but the player's bags were scattered around. If I touched the wrong bag I would have gotten in trouble. I don't think that somebody else would have had the same problem.

Sports and school became more difficult in the seventh grade. I joined the cross-country track and lacrosse teams, which were harder than I was used to because of the confusing verbal directions. If the coach actually showed me what to do I was able to do it without any misunderstanding.

I attended Hebrew School three days a week for my Bar Mitzvah after completing my regular school. Learning and speaking Hebrew was very difficult. The special symbols that I had to learn in order to read my Haftorah (section of the bible) for my Bar Mitzvah were extremely difficult to do. The Hebrew alphabet has different symbols and letters than the English alphabet and I found it very difficult to read.

My seventh grade teachers did not take the special time to work with me as my sixth grade ones did. One Science teacher was actually mean. She did not want to offer me my accommodations, and would penalize me for any homework misunderstandings and almost always had an excuse not to give me any extra help. I even went to school early for extra help in math and English and during my lunch period for ASL, American Sign Language.

One other problem was my ASL class. The teacher left after two months to have a baby. After that time, we had a bunch of substitutes who did not teach any ASL. Finally, we got a new ASL teacher who taught differently. She had a different type ASL dialect and I became confused and sad. Four months later, my original ASL teacher returned, and she worked closely with me to get me up to speed. I felt special because she did not really help other students the way she helped me. She rearranged her schedule to help me. This teacher made me feel good the way that she helped me, and during her class I did not feel stupid.

One factor in my life that I felt was different for me than for other kids my age was that I felt I was constantly going to school. I would get up early for extra help, go to school, do school sports after school, then go to Hebrew School. When I would get home from Hebrew School I would do my homework, and finally go to sleep and do it all over again the next day. On the weekends, I went to Temple and Hebrew School, finished my homework and studied for Monday's tests. Very often I felt sad and burnt out. I felt like my brain was on fire and wouldn't work correctly. I'd be overwhelmed and would call my dad at work in the middle of the day at school. He would help calm me down and explain things so I could attempt them easier and without so much pressure.

A positive thing that occurred was that I was allowed to take my tests in the office of the Assistant Principal. He became my friend and someone whom I could count on, when I was confused and overwhelmed. We talked a lot especially when I was having problems with my classmates, sports and teachers. He would encourage me and seemed genuinely happy when I got good grades.

In the eighth grade, the teacher's talked about getting ready for the State tests. There was one for every subject. It was really intense. I studied at school and at night and took special classes. These classes reviewed the work at a pace that I could not keep up with. The study booklets they gave us were very confusing at first, but later I used them with my speech therapist. When I went over them at a slower pace, with her, they were helpful.

A big problem that occurred in middle school was when my chorus teacher took me out of my main classes for vocal lessons. This made me very nervous and mad. I felt that I would not be able to catch up with the class and I would miss a lot of work. She would not let me come early, stay late or do the lesson during gym, lunch or art. My parents argued with her a lot which made me feel she was mad at me or that she picked on me for no reason in class.

When a teacher is too tense I become agitated and then I make errors. Every noise gives me a headache and I forget things. My art and technology teachers would blame me for things I did not do or not help me when I could not find something I needed. I missed the teachers I had in sixth grade and appreciated the ones I had who went out of their ways to understand me.

I really looked forward to gym. The gym teacher was cool, and made me feel comfortable. When I did not understand the directions, she helped explain them without embarrassing me. If I fell or did something wrong, she'd tell a silly joke and make everybody laugh which took the pressure off me. I couldn't wait to go to High School because, hopefully, the teachers would understand me better.

I also liked going to work with my dad. When you sell, like my father does, you convince someone to buy something by reading their movements and by their facial expressions. With no distractions, it's easy to talk with people. It's harder to sell on the phone because you can't see them so you have to concentrate on their voices and what they say.

This is the reason I like sports, too. It is interactive, competitive and very visual. If you read the movements of the others players correctly you have a better chance to win.

High school became infinitely harder than middle school for me. But in some ways it became easier. My guidance counselor and the school psychologist arranged for many of my accommodations to take place. However the specifics of these often came with hidden problems and I needed to advocate for myself even more. As opposed to middle school where I had one teacher for each subject for the whole year, high school was completely different. I had some teachers for only half of the school year and a different teacher for the second half.

My parents had a "team" meeting with most of my teachers about three to six weeks after the semester began to discuss my accommodations with the school psychologist, guidance counselor and teachers. A teacher who knew me from the previous year would sometimes come to the meeting. Many teachers were willing to try different things to help me learn, but there were always one or two difficult ones. My mom explained my problems and my dad gave them examples of my auditory processing disorder as it pertained to their specific class. Many times my parents saw the teachers finally grasp the situation.

In my senior year, I got to sit in on the teacher team meeting with my parents. At first I felt awkward, because I had spent over a month with all of them, some of whom, like American Sign Language and English much longer. However, I also felt strangely confident. My mother had grilled me over and over about my disorder and what my accommodations were and the reasons I needed them. This was only to be a small sampling of what I would be up against when I would have my solo interviews with the learning disability departments for the colleges that I hoped to attend.

For the most part the meeting went well and the school psychologist directed many of the questions to me. The only time my parents chimed in was to offer further clarification or insight. I listened to them intently, as to try to make note of them, because I knew I would need this vital information later to explain to the colleges what I needed to help with my academics. This meeting was necessary both for my teachers and me because it helped set up an entire year with the least amount of aggravation that I might encounter.

"Separate room testing" was pre-arranged between the teacher, the school's proctor and me but sometimes the room was changed at the last minute and I was not told ahead of time. "Minimal distractions" helped, except when people talked in the hall, or when the proctor's two-way radio kept going off, or some student in the room clicked their pen over and over.

"Rephrasing the questions" was a good accommodation but mainly if it was my teacher giving me the test themselves. If there was a proctor, many times they could not rephrase the questions properly, which caused me to give a wrong answer many times.

"Restating the directions" helped, but could take up a lot of my extra time. I was allowed "extra time" or time and a half as it was also called, to process information. If a non-learning disabled student got 60 minutes, I got ninety minutes for the same test, to allow time for all of my accommodations.

Some teachers really used their heads to accommodate me. If my English teacher was going to give an oral quiz, he would have a copy of the questions for me written out so I could do them at my pace and not have to leave the class. Many of my teachers wrote out homework assignments on the blackboard and remind me to copy them before I left the class. I kept a second set of text books at home in case I forgot them in my locker, due to my short-term memory loss.

Many teachers understood my learning difficulties but there were others who made my life miserable. One teacher would give essays and tests on Fridays. If I couldn't finish in one period, and needed extra time and arranged to finish the test on Monday, they would want to give me a new "make-up" test so that I could not look up the answers over the weekend. Many times I forgot my homework in my locker and if I went to retrieve it on the way to class, I might be late and be penalized for being late. But if I came to class and the teacher was in a bad mood, they would not let me go get it and then I would be penalized too. One teacher actually said, "auditory processing disorders are made up by school psychologists to keep them busy when there isn't anything more important to do."

Gym class was a nightmare at times. All the kids talking, joking and moving around drowned out the teachers instructions. If the coach or teacher would shouted commands at me from across the field, most times I couldn't hear any or all of it which then caused me to get into trouble for not doing the task correctly. I finally had to advocate for myself and worked out solutions to this and similar situations.

If I attended a power point presentation or a science lab demonstration, I made sure I stood right next to the teacher, for optimum understanding. When it came to library work, computer classes, or craft art classes, I got "preferential seating" next to the teacher. This worked well in some other classes like Sports Marketing, Health and Business. However, it did not work well for others like Social Studies or Science. The teachers would walk up and down the rows talking and asking questions to the students. These conditions made it difficult for me to concentrate so I often needed private tutors.

I took American Sign Language to fill my language requirement. There was mainly a visual component with very little auditory learning. It was similar to karate where you needed to hold your hands and fingers a particular way and remember the steps. But the language and sentence structure aspect was hard to comprehend at times.

I was very lucky when I got a teacher who I had in a previous class because they knew how to work with me. Or when a person who was my private tutor previously later actually became my teacher. This made my life easier because they were familiar with my capabilities.

Many of my subjects in high school proved to be very difficult. On almost a daily basis I would go for extra help in school. Sometimes, if the teacher was available before school started, I worked with them. This was extremely helpful because it locked in the information that I needed for that day or for a test.

In addition to the extra help, I had lots of private tutoring, sometimes four to five days a week. Especially in my junior year where I had to take three state tests (Regents), four important finals and the SAT and ACT tests. The Regents and final grades were vital to my graduation and class ranking. I even had two-hour double sessions just before the tests. It was very, very, hard to concentrate. Some days I felt like my head would explode and I often had to go to the nurse's office, which was quiet and calm, to sort of decompress. In the end, I did fairly well. I was a solid B plus student, due very much in part by the unrelenting urgings, confidence and support of my parents.

As I got older, I had to advocate for myself more. I needed to make sure that I received my accommodations on an almost daily basis. My guidance counselor became a huge help in easing my auditory difficulties. To avoid "auditory overload" she did not schedule the more difficult classes at the end of the day. Instead she started them at the beginning of the day and inserted an easy class like Gym, Crafts or Marketing in between. My schedule became less intense as the day progressed which made my life somewhat easier. Besides having lunch in the middle of my day, which helped relax my auditory sensors, she also arranged for a free period every other day. This allowed me to finish taking tests when I needed the extra time.

The major problems in high school actually came from state tests and my accommodations in relation to taking them. Getting my accommodations for the Regents, SAT and ACT exams were a nightmare for my parents. They were denied for the ACT test but my mother fought "tooth and nail" to get my extended time. The SAT test was super hard and I actually did worse the second time I took it.

My tutor was fantastic and worked very closely with me. I had realized that the SAT prep classes were not for me because the pace of the classes were too fast for me. I also found that they did not like it when students asked a lot of questions like I tended to do. With my tutor I did not have to be afraid of embarrassing myself with a wrong answer or asking what they considered to be a silly question. My tutor saw that I was better at Science and general knowledge, than in Math and English grammar. So she put a lot of our focus in those areas. The result was that I went from an 18 on my first ACT to a 22 on my second ACT test, which was a huge jump. In my opinion this was the main reason I got accepted to the college of my choice. It also helped me excel in some of my school subjects as well.

I needed to be retested in my Junior year, so that I could apply to certain Learning Disability Programs. This cost my parents a lot of money, but it was necessary for me to be accepted into many of the college's learning disability programs. One state college, only wanted to give me accommodations for English and Math classes, as if my auditory processing only failed to work for those two subjects. The problem was I needed accommodations for all of my subjects and not many schools were willing to grant that.

Some schools would not give me language credit for taking American Sign Language. ASL is a visual language, no real sound. Without that course, I never would have been able to understand other languages with my APD.

I had to be interviewed privately by the administrators of the disabilities departments of the colleges before they would accept me or agree to my accommodations. My parents were not allowed in the room for back-up and/or support which made the interviews more stressful for me. The interviews were intense sometimes and the interviewer wanted specific information. Fortunately, my mom had gone over this information with me prior to the interview.

The Learning Disability Programs seemed to understand my APD symptoms when they were compared to some symptoms of Attention Deficit Disorder which they were more familiar with. The state colleges were very reluctant to honor any of my accommodations, while the private schools were willing to accommodate my auditory processing disorder, provided my parents were willing to give them extra money to do this.

Besides the intense interviews with the disabilities departments, we visited many of the colleges and met with many people. Although the tours were interesting my auditory processing disorder, made it very difficult to follow all the information given by the guides at the regular open houses.

For example, a guide would say in a low monotone voice, "Here's Binky Hall, where you will have all your Science classes unless you have Forensics or Chemistry. And then there is Brownstone Hall where we keep the research, blah, blah, blah bibbity and so on." It was just too much information to process in a short time, plus other noise distractions.

I would ask questions about things that peaked my interest. I was able to store the information I needed much easier on the one-on-one tours. I made mental notes, about the positives and negatives. Negatives were more important to remember. If there were a lot of lecture halls, I would not be able to learn in that type of situation. I also wondered if I would be required to take a language class, and who did their tutoring and how did it work, not to mention what accommodations I would be given if I made the Lacrosse team. These were some of the questions that I needed answers to. You see, some colleges make you study or do homework on the way to and from your away sport games. I could never be able to concentrate on a bus full of rowdy players with my APD. The college I eventually chose would need to accommodate me better to avoid any of the learning pitfalls so that my grades would not suffer.

Socially, my high school experience improved as I got older. Physical fighting because of auditory misunderstandings with my friends became a thing of the past. I learned how to compensate for many of my auditory short comings with teammates and females. As communicating through e-mails and phone texting became more popular, so did I.

Although my days were better when I was in high school than when I was in middle school, there were many times that I hid in the school nurse's office, to decompress and come back to myself so that I could return to the front lines.

It is amazing to think about the battles and wars, that my mother and grandfather had to fight with their APD in school. However, they both finished college and even went further to fulfill their career requirements. I know that I am destined to do the same. I look to my future and know that I will still have to advocate for myself.

But thanks to the others who came before me, it will be a lot easier as time goes on.

As I grow older, I hope that teachers learn to understand APD problems and needs that will help children instead of making them feel stupid.

Chapter Seven

A Mothers Experience
Advocating for a Child
with Auditory Processing Disorders

by Lorraine Alderman, Psy.D.

My son Andrew has auditory processing problems. My interest in and awareness of Auditory Processing Disorders (APD)started because of my son's problems. While I was in graduate school, I noticed that Andrew was having some difficulties verbalizing his needs and wants. He tended to point to things that he wanted as opposed to using words. My son also tended to over-react to things, and that did not make sense to me.

When he was about two and a half years of age, I distinctly remember that I started to point to my ear when talking to him and said the word "listen" to get his attention. After doing so a few times, he seemed to understand that I was indicating that he had previously misinterpreted or inappropriately responded to something I had just said to him. Over the next few years, I kept asking his various nursery and preschool teachers if they noticed any difficulties with Andrew, and if they thought I should get a speech-language evaluation for him? Each of his teachers, as well as my husband, basically told me that Andrew was fine, and that I was being overprotective of him.

The year before my son was supposed to start kindergarten, I had him tested for the gifted program in our district. I thought that it was not a good sign when the examiner from the district brought him back to me only fifteen minutes after starting the assessment. I was upset when he didn't make the program. I was convinced that the person from the district was inexperienced and had made some error. When I tried to get details of the assessment, I was told that I could not get any.

I decided to take him to a private examiner where I could at least get a report of the findings. Well, there was no mistake that his intelligence was in the average range and the district wanted the higher end of the high average range. I was disappointed and resigned myself to putting him into a regular kindergarten class.

When he started kindergarten, he was in a new grant-funded program based on the multiple intelligence model. There have been many proposed theories of intelligence over the years. The traditional theory of intelligence views it as a single entity and that a person is born with a certain level of intelligence that cannot be altered in a significant way. Howard Gardner (Howard Gardner. Multiple Intelligence: The Theory in Practice. Basic Books 1993) proposed a theory of multiple intelligence's. He believes that there are multiple forms of intelligence that enable each person to become a competent individual. Some of the forms of intelligence in his theory are: linguistic and logical, musical, spatial, bodily-kinesthetic, naturalistic, interpersonal and existential. For example, a talented musician would be considered to have a high musical form of intelligence in Howard Gardner's model of multiple intelligences.

As my son's kindergarten year progressed, I noticed that he was not learning the concepts being taught in school. It was December and he still did not have the concept of the days of the week and could not write his name. Finally, in February of his kindergarten year of school, his teacher agreed that something was wrong. She admitted to me that she had felt that something was wrong back in November, however, her supervisor told her to concentrate on my son's strengths as opposed to his weaknesses. Since playing with things was a strength for Andrew, I'm assuming that the supervisor wanted the teacher to focus on his spatial and bodily-kinesthetic strengths as a way of trying to teach him. Thus, he may have been more "intelligent" as a spatial/bodily-kinesthetic learner than as the more educationally traditional visual or auditory learner.

His teacher also related that she was reading a book about "processing disorders" and thought that it had described Andrew and his difficulties. With a letter from my son's teacher suggesting that he needed a speech-language evaluation, my husband agreed to let me take him for one.

In my opinion, Andrew's kindergarten teacher (she was also his second grade teacher) appeared to be a very competent teacher, so I do not know how much of Andrew's lack of progress was influenced by:

1) His teacher not correctly implementing Howard Gardner's theories and focusing on teaching Andrew using spatial and body/kinesthetic activities, and

2) how much Andrew's auditory processing difficulties caused problems learning.

After receiving the letter from Andrew's teacher, I found a speech-language pathologist through my insurance and made an appointment. After her evaluation, she told me that my son really did have a problem and that she would see him for speech-language therapy once a week over the next 12 weeks. I asked what would happen at the end of the 12 weeks? She didn't fully answer my question, but indicated that the insurance wouldn't cover anything after 12 weeks. I left with a very uneasy feeling.

Although the speech-language pathologist confirmed that something was wrong with my son, it did not make sense that it would be cured in 12 weeks when, coincidentally, the insurance coverage would end. The speech-language pathologist also did not quite answer my questions as to what specifically was wrong with my son.

After talking with a friend whose son was in speech-language therapy, she suggested that I have my son reevaluated by her son's speech-language pathologist. This particular pathologist offered a free 20-minute screening for new clients. I figured that I didn't have anything to lose, so I set up an appointment.

My son spent a half hour with this speech-language pathologist. She then came out and explained to my husband and I that our son had a "processing disorder." She indicated that further testing would give us more specific information about his specific processing difficulties. The speech-language pathologist then went on to explain how speech-language therapy would help him and that it would be a life-long process. She also explained that it wasn't so much speech-language therapy per se, it was really therapy for processing difficulties related to speech and sounds.

I left there feeling that I finally had some answers that made sense. Andrew started speech therapy that summer. Additionally, I took him for a neuropsychological evaluation. I figured that I wanted to cover all my bases. Being new to the field of psychology, I asked one of my psychology supervisors for a recommendation. Although I had outpatient and inpatient experience and had spent two years interning in a school district, I was very nervous about the whole neuropsychological assessment. So nervous, that I showed up on the wrong day for Andrew's appointment! After the testing was completed, I could not wait for the next appointment at which the evaluator would give my husband and me the results.

At that time, I had already completed my doctorate in school/community psychology. But, as I sat there listening to this person to give me the results, all I heard was the recommendation to put him into special education along with therapy to help him cope with his difficulties in learning. The next day, I went over the report with my supervisor at the hospital where I was working. I had only briefly heard while in graduate school about several of the tests that my son was given because I did not follow the neuropsychological track of study.

My supervisor went over each of the tests with me step by step, explaining the results and what they meant. I soon realized that many of the tests administered required that my son have a good understanding of the alphabet, good sequencing skills and good auditory memory abilities, all of which he did not have.

He had left kindergarten not knowing the alphabet because his teacher was told by her supervisor not to worry about it and to teach to his strengths (playing was his strength, not academics).

I felt that if he really needed special education I would eventually agree to have him placed in such a program, but I was not going to do so without first trying to teach him the basics.

Having completed a school psychology program, one of the things that you learn is not to put a child into special education due to a lack of education. Although my son attended schools since the age of two years, no one had taught him the alphabet because he always preferred to play and probably gave his teachers a hard time when they tried to teach it to him. Therefore, I rejected the recommendation for special education and spent the summer teaching my son the alphabet.

My son's tolerance level was very low and his frustration level was very high, and I could understand why his teachers found it easier to let him play than to try and teach him the alphabet. We did on an average of three letters a day with the promise of getting to do some bowling if he cooperated. He also started speech-language therapy working on building his vocabulary and sequencing skills. Additionally, the speech-language pathologist suggested activities that I could do with Andrew to help build his vocabulary and his ability to categorize.

I had to verbally describe what I was doing while cooking such as saying all the steps in the process (such as stirring, the texture of the food, etc.) and I had to verbalize things such as how carrots and celery were both vegetables when I went food shopping with Andrew. I know it sounds as if my son were really slow. However, because he communicated primarily through pointing, and my husband and I allowed that mode to be accepted, Andrew never really developed his oral vocabulary.

When he went into the first grade, Andrew's speech-language pathologist, whom he was seeing outside of school, went to his school to talk to with his teacher. The speech-language pathologist tried to explain to his teacher some of Andrew's difficulties and the best ways to work with him. Andrew struggled but was able to stay afloat.

In second grade, he had his former kindergarten teacher as his classroom teacher. She is the only teacher he has had who could tell when Andrew would respond to a question whether he did or did not have a clue as to what was being asked by reading Andrew's body cues and facial expressions. Therefore, she was able to work very productively with him. After my son completed second grade, we moved from Brooklyn, New York to Long Island, New York and out of the

New York City Board of Education public school system. Because the expectations were higher at his new school, I started to work with him on his reading during the summer in order to help prepare him for the upcoming school year. As the school year progressed, he started to have difficulties following directions, completing tasks and he had difficulty understanding concepts that were being taught in school.

Andrew was still attending weekly speech-language therapy sessions paid for by a private health insurance provider. I hesitated getting him speech-language therapy through the school system for several reasons. I had interned as a school psychologist in schools in Long Island, I felt that, based on the severity of his issues, the most therapy I could hope for was once a week for 15 to 30 minutes in a group of three to five students. Additionally, with school vacation breaks (winter vacation, President's week, spring vacation, summer vacation, etc.) he would miss over three months of therapy sessions. I did not feel that therapy, in this form, would make a significant difference and I did not want him to miss time from his classes.

About the time that I was starting to feel really frustrated about his situation, I spoke with a friend who had been in my graduate program. She had started working in the schools after graduation while I worked in a hospital setting. My friend listened as I talked about the difficulties my son was having. "Does Andrew have any Section 504 accommodations?" Dena asked. "Section 504 what?" I asked. "I've never heard of that before." "Some children do not need special education but do need some testing accommodations to level the playing field." Dena said. "You can get those accommodations under what is known as Section 504." *(Note that Section 504 of the Rehabilitation Act of 1973 is one of many legal documents protecting the rights of children with educational disabilities to obtain equal access to education.)* "I wonder if that could be the solution Andrew needs." I said excitedly. With the information that my friend gave to me, I learned that the school could use data from the testing that was done privately to determine my son's eligibility for a Section 504 Plan. (Note that some schools insist that they do some of their own testing. However, according to the Individuals with Disabilities Education

Act (IDEA), you are allowed to use a private evaluator at your own expense without consulting the school district.) The first meeting that took place with the school district went relatively well mainly because my husband and I did not ask for much in terms of our son's accommodations. His first set of Section 504 accommodations consisted of the following, Andrew would:

1. Be provided with extended time (time and a half) for tests.
2. Be provided with preferential seating (near the teacher and blackboard)
3. Have directions and questions re-read and rephrased or explained to him in detail because of language processing difficulties, and
4. Be allowed to restate those directions and questions in his own words to assess his understanding of the instructions.

These accommodations were put in place in January of his third grade year. Although his teacher was very young and inexperienced, she actually implemented his accommodations better than his more experienced teachers did over the following years.

Around the time Andrew received his first set of accommodations, I started to become more aware and involved in his schoolwork. At that point in time, I had finished graduate school as well as my clinical internship, doctoral dissertation, post-doctorate year, and studied for and passed my licensing exam. Therefore, my attention was now able to be focused more on my son's schooling. On open school night, his third grade teacher related that Andrew would avoid individual quiet reading time like it was "the plague." He would make trips back and forth to his knapsack or to the bathroom and would end up not spending any real time reading.

I asked the teacher to show me the book they had chosen for him to read independently. When I looked over the book, I realized that it was at least two grade levels above his current reading level. For a child who had very little if any tolerance for frustration, it was not rocket science to understand why he avoided reading. The next day, I sent him in with a book that was just below his current reading level. He went from reading one book in the first half of the school year to reading eleven books the second half of the school year.

I also started a reading incentive program at home. For every seven pages of a book he read with me, he could have a pack of baseball cards. I bought the baseball cards by the box, so that he could get immediate reinforcement when he finished reading. As he progressed in his reading, we increased this reward to every 10 or 12 pages depending on the size of the print in the book. I also let him get any magazine that he wanted to read so long it had more words than pictures in it.

Now, when I work with parents in my school, I often recommend that they sit and read with their child and that they set up a positive reward system. I compare this system to giving a child a piece of candy to get rid of the bad taste after they take medicine. For my son and other students who have difficulties reading, the idea of reading is more distressing to them than the idea of taking bitter-tasting medicine. Because of the positive reinforcement provided and the accommodations being followed, by the end of the third grade, Andrew's grades started to improve and he started to feel better about himself. At the end of the second week of school, when Andrew started the fourth grade, I asked his teacher if she had any questions about his accommodations. "He has accommodations?" she asked. I then realized that I could not leave things totally in the hands of the school. I had to advocate on behalf of my son if his ongoing needs were to be met. I called the school psychologist and said that I wanted to have a meeting with Andrew's teacher, myself, and Andrew's speech-language therapist so that his teacher could not only have an understanding of his accommodations, but also of how to work best with Andrew.

At the same time, I suggested that although the renewal date for his accommodations was not till January, we do this review and renew his accommodations at the same meeting. Section 504 accommodations must be renewed every year; they do not roll over the way accommodations on an Individualized Educational Plan (IEP) do for children who are classified under IDEA.

I guess the school felt threatened because they had his reading teacher, the speech-language therapist for the school, who had never met my son, and the principal of the school at this meeting. Bringing Andrew's private speech-language pathologist to the meeting was extremely beneficial. She was able to explain to the teacher Andrew's specific needs and able to respond to questions from the school's speech-language therapist who believed that Auditory Processing Disorders were "just a fad." You might get the feeling that the fourth grade was an important year based on the amount of time that I'm devoting to it. However, I am devoting so much time to it because was a rough experience to put it lightly. Around this time, New York State started to give fourth graders a new English Language Arts (ELA) exam. This was a big deal because all the area newspapers published the scores for every school. The test had a new format and there was a great deal of concern about children's abilities to score well on this exam because the students taking it in the first few years did not have the classroom instruction that accompanied the new format for the exam.

Children who were first starting kindergarten were being taught the new style of the test. Many rumors also circulated about the test, that children failing the test would go to summer school or would be left back if they did not perform well. Needless to say, if the average parent were nervous about the test, my anxiety was "through the roof."

The test involved reading, writing, listening to an orally read story and responding to written questions about the story, making inferences, and understanding idioms. Most of these tasks Andrew could not do well. I hired a private tutor to work with him over the summer after the third grade and through the first few months of fourth grade. Additionally, his speech-language pathologist worked with him on understanding idioms. We basically taught him how to take the test. The scores were on a scale of one to four with four being the highest level of achievement. Andrew scored a three.

As if the ELA testing was not stressful enough, fourth graders also had to take a relatively new math statewide test. When Andrew came home from school after taking the math statewide test, he told me that he had taken the test in a different room from his class. I was happy because I realized that the school had just set a precedent for him. That is, they allowed him to take his tests in a separate location that provided minimal distractions. This opened the opportunity to add "testing in a separate location" to his section 504 accommodations the following year.

From the time Andrew was given Section 504 accommodations, the issue of how to implement the accommodations regarding providing extra time and restating questions for Andrew was always at issue. His principal refused to give him resource room (a service in which children classified under IDEA usually receive extra help one period a day and take their tests in this room). Providing Andrew with resource room would have solved the problem of Andrew receiving extra time on tests without any class distractions because he would always have a place in which to take his tests, i.e.; the resource room. Additionally, it would have solved the problem with a proctor being able to rephrase questions without drawing attention to Andrew. Now looking forward to next year's Section 504 meeting because I was going to add a "separate location for testing" accommodation.

After my experience with Andrew's fourth grade teacher not knowing for the first two weeks about his accommodations, I decided to be pro-active. I spent time that summer surfing the internet for information about Auditory Processing Disorders (APD). I took what I considered to be the best information from each of the web sites and made a handout on APD citing each of the sources. I tried to keep the handout very simple. I then went to school two days before Andrew started fifth grade and met with his teacher. I gave him the handout that I had made along with a copy of Andrew's accommodations and described Andrew's his special needs. I also indicated that his speech-language pathologist would be coming to a meeting soon after school started. I told his teacher that if he had any questions, he could feel free to call Andrew's speech-language pathologist or me.

This meeting took place on Monday, and Andrew started school on Wednesday. By Friday, everything that I had done with his teacher had gone "out the window." Andrew came home and informed me that he was given a math placement test to determine which math class he would take for the entire school year. He also told me that his teacher told him that he wanted to "see what he could do," and that is why the teacher would not give Andrew any of his accommodations.

When I called his school, I have to say I was fuming. Their response to me did not help. I was told that my son had made the "average" math group, and they really did not understand why I was so upset. "It's not like he made the low average group," they added.

Now, just for a point of fact, I am 100 percent fine with my son being "average." The reason I was upset was that I had personally made his teacher aware of Andrew's accommodations and in less than a week I found that our conversation had no impact on the teacher whatsoever. Many times since then, I felt that I should have sued his teacher in civil court for clearly breaking my son's civil rights. However, I live in a small community and didn't want the publicity and stigmatism that would have gone along with the lawsuit, even though it may have been justified.

Three weeks later, we had Andrew's fifth grade meeting to renew his Section 504 accommodations. I went to the meeting with the intent of letting everyone know that I was still upset over the math test situation, and that I wanted to add "testing to be provided in a small group setting" to his present accommodations.

Prior to the meeting, I had a strategy and planning meeting with Andrew's speech-language pathologist. We agreed that if the school did not give us the new addition to Andrew's accommodations, we would abruptly end the meeting and start an appeal process. (Note: Every school district has to have an appeal process available to parents when the school and the parents do not agree with the outcome of a 504 meeting or the provision of services such as accommodations under Section 504).

I told my husband of this strategy, and he promised not to get into an argument with the principal. Well, so much for planning. When the principal refused to add the "separate location for testing" accommodation, I, a certified school psychologist and licensed clinical psychologist, lost my temper and started raising my voice as my husband was politely trying to remind me of our plan. We live across the street from that school and I left the principal's office stating that the appeal process would start within the next five minutes, which it was.

After contacting the head psychologist of the school district, I explained to her that:

1. The principal's request to update Andrew's intelligence testing did not make sense because updating his intelligence score was not going to change the fact that he had APD.

2. The precedent for testing in a separate location had been set last year by the school when Andrew took the math statewide test and that by law you cannot have one set of accommodations for classroom tests and another for statewide tests.

3. The mess up with his math placement test earlier in the year would likely lead to my winning a law suit if I sued for violation of my son's civil rights under Section 504 of the Rehabilitation Act.

With all of this information, she said she would have to speak to "the school" and gather more information, and then she would get back in touch with me. In the meantime, I met with a lawyer who advised me to have my son classified under IDEA because it would make life easier. His reasoning was that teachers and schools tend to pay more attention to Individualized Educational Plans (IEP's) than they do to Section 504 Plans.

This was not an acceptable reason for me to have my son classified under IDEA when his needs could be met through accommodations under Section 504 of the Rehabilitation Act. The reason why I wanted his testing to take place in a separate location was because of the high level of distractibility present when Andrew took tests in his classroom. His teachers had him taking his tests sitting by their desks. Every time another teacher walked in the room to talk to one of his teachers, or every time the teacher had to tend to another student in the class, Andrew's testing was disrupted and he would often lose his train of thought.

Having not heard from the head psychologist for two weeks, I called her to follow-up. She informed me that she was still waiting for the papers from Andrew's school. I asked her for her fax number and told her that I would send her copies of everything within the next ten minutes. I also informed her that I had met with a lawyer and was going to do whatever was necessary in order to get my son the accommodations he needed.

The very next day I received a phone call from her indicating that the school would contact me about reconvening the Section 504 meeting. My experience with working in different schools had taught me that many districts do not want cases to go to arbitration because it costs them money to have their lawyers involved.

In the above case, the principal was not happy that he had lost the "battle." He walked into the conference room with a four-inch stack of papers and slammed them down on the table. He then pointed to one page that had the results of Andrew's math state test and said, "See, Andrew's a bright boy, he's polite and he always says hello to me in the hallway." I responded by saying that I never said that my son he was not smart or well mannered and that I know that he was not a behavior problem, neither of which changed the fact that he has APD and needed accommodations for learning and for taking tests.

When it came time for Andrew to graduate from elementary school at the end of the fifth grade, I was happy to be out of his elementary school, yet terrified at the thought of having to deal with several middle school teachers and getting them to do what I could not get one elementary teacher to do properly.

Fortunately, Andrew was very lucky and was placed with a fabulous team of teachers for sixth grade. We still had a few minor difficulties now and then, but, in general, it went a lot better than I had anticipated.

Some of the difficulties we encountered, centered more around Andrew's organizational skills (or lack thereof) and problems with his reasoning abilities. I had to rewrite his schedule in several differ-ent formats before we found a format that he could follow with ease.

Because students were only allowed to go to their lockers during certain periods, we had to help him figure out which books he needed to take out of his locker for classes during the specific times that he was allowed to go to his locker. His school also had a "no back pack" rule, meaning that students were not allowed to carry their knapsacks around from class-to-class during the school day. We had to find an organizer that held his planner book (schedule/calendar book), his folders his pen's etc., and one that he could carry through out the day. My husband and I found a binder/organizer made by Mead. It was made of black canvas material with several sections to it. On the front was a zippered pocket for pens and a calculator. Then there was a compartment that held two marble composition notebooks. The binder area was big enough to hold his daily planner book and a folder for each subject. The binder area also had a zipper to secure pages in the binder from being lost.

Andrew's sixth grade year was probably the best year of school for him because of the group of teachers he had. For example, his social studies teacher had the students "live" each of the eras about which they learned. So they were cavemen, Egyptians, Greeks, and so on. This added a component which really helped Andrew learn by using visual and kinesthetic aspects to learning history (i.e., learning by seeing and doing). As I had done in elementary school, I renewed his Section 504 accommodations at the beginning of the school year and requested that each of his teachers be present so that they could learn how to work appropriately with Andrew.

Two areas of concern for me at that meeting were:

1. Andrew was taking a chorus class that required him to miss academic classes four times a marking period for vocal lessons, and

2. Having Andrew be required to copy notes (in his health class) from the overhead projected image while the teacher was teaching her lesson.

Andrew expressed concerns about his ability to make-up the missed work and not fall behind when he had to miss academic classes for vocal lessons. He wanted to come to school early, give up a lunch or gym period, or stay after school to do the vocal lessons. Furthermore, Andrew had concerns with his health class, regarding the fact that he could either copy the notes or follow the lesson but he could not do both at the same time. Therefore, we needed him to have a copy of the notes provided by his health class teacher so Andrew could pay attention to the verbal lessons.

The school accommodated us with the notes, but would not compromise about having vocal lessons before or after the school day or during his lunch or gym period. Instead, his guidance counselor told me that she would "do me a favor" and put him into a general music class instead of chorus.

Andrew liked chorus because it was not like a "regular" class, and he did not want general music where he had to sit and take notes in a classroom. I told the people at the meeting that we would give the vocal lessons a try and see how missing four academic classes a marking period affected Andrew. That was a decision that came back to haunt me throughout the next three years while he was in middle school.

Rather than presenting a compromise on my end, I should have hired a lawyer and fought the requirement of the vocal lessons. (Note: In our school district, you cannot pass chorus unless you attend the vocal lessons and two evening performances given by the chorus.)

Based on my conversations with parents from the Special Education Parent Teachers Association (SEPTA) in our area, I may have won that accommodation had I decided to fight for it and not compromise. Their reasoning was that chorus was good for Andrew's self-esteem and there should be times other than when he has an academic class that he could have a vocal lesson. Sometimes you get tired of fighting and you have to decide to pick and choose your battles, so I did not pick this battle to fight much to my dismay later.

In seventh grade, I wanted to add two new accommodations to Andrew's 504 Plan. As children grow their needs change and their accommodations need to adapt to these changes. My husband and I found that over the past few years, Andrew had difficulty generalizing information. In other words, he could not simply read over his notes or textbook and then be able to answer multiple choice questions or fill-in questions on a test. To help him prepare for tests, my husband and I made up practice tests for him. Most of his teachers cooperated by telling him the format of tests beforehand.

However, some teachers refused to do so. Therefore, I wanted to add "obtaining the format of tests from teachers" to Andrew's list of accommodations. I realized this was not the best solution to the problem, but only an immediate assistance. We are now working with Andrew and various tutors to help him be able to generalize information and learn other ways of studying. The school team did not give me a hard time with the request for this new accommodation.

The second accommodation that I wanted to add was to have a second set of textbooks at home. When Andrew was in elementary school, it was across the street from our house making it easier to go back to school to get what Andrew had forgotten when he came home from school. Andrew would often forget a book he needed to do his homework assignments. Now his school was almost two miles away from our house. Additionally, his knapsack weighed over 25 pounds on any given day and he weighed about 68 pounds. I felt that it was ridiculous to carry books that weighed that much back and forth each day. The school said that the only way they would add this request to his accommodations were if I obtained a doctor's note stating that Andrew needed a second set of books for medical reasons. The school said that they were afraid that a second set of books at home would create a dependency. My doctor readily wrote the note, and after about two weeks we received the duplicate books.

One aspect of his seventh grade Section 504 renewal and teacher information meeting was totally new to us and was actually a change for the better. The school psychologist suggested that one of his teachers from the sixth grade attend the meeting along with the other people who were to attend.

Initially, I was a little hesitant about this change because I did not know which teacher would be at there, and if we would be lucky enough to get one who had worked well with him in the past. However, it turned out to be a positive addition to the meeting.

The previous year's teacher informed Andrew's seventh grade teachers that he was a student who was always willing to come in early and/or stay late after school in order to receive the extra help that he needed. His sixth grade teacher also talked about his personality and how Andrew was basically a good kid who found himself in trouble at times usually due to a verbal misunderstanding. She also related that my husband and I were very involved in his education, and we could always be reached if there were ever any difficulties or concerns.

His eighth grade meeting was almost identical to his seventh grade meeting with the exception of the presence of one of the assistant principals. This was a good addition. This assistant principal befriended my son toward the end of the sixth grade and was like a mentor, counselor and guardian angel all rolled into one. Andrew first met him because they would use his office as the place for Andrew to take his tests in order to meet his accommodations of a separate testing location and extended time on tests. However, this was only the tip of the iceberg of their relationship.

A perfect example of how Andrew's misinterpretations can turn a good event into a bad situation came out during this eighth grade meeting. The assistant principal was providing an example to Andrew's new teachers of how he was a good kid with good character traits. He then related how Andrew had found an expensive watch in the boy's locker room and was afraid that if he put the watch in the Lost-and-Found box someone would steal it. So, instead, Andrew gave the watch directly to him. As a reward for his honesty, the assistant principal said that he was going to give Andrew a certificate to get free Carvel ice cream the following Friday.

As he said this, my husband and I looked at each other with an "oh no" look. Andrew went to the lunch lady the very day that he was told by the assistant principal about the free Carvel ice cream. He missed the part about getting the certificate and waiting until Friday. He told the lunch lady that the assistant principal said that he could have a free Carvel ice cream. The lunch lady called him a liar and would not give him anything.

Instead of feeling good about the whole situation, Andrew felt sad and upset. When the assistant principal told him about the ice cream award, Andrew did not process the part about coming to him the next morning to "get a certificate to use the following Friday." The assistant principal turned to Andrew's new teachers and said that this was typical of how Andrew could misunderstand what has been said to him. He further explained how a seemingly good thing could easily go awry based on Andrew's APD.

At times, over the three year period in the middle school, Andrew would get into predicaments or run into difficulties. When he did, it was usually one of four scenarios.

1. He got into trouble for talking in class because he would ask kids to stop clicking or tapping their pens because he could not block out the noise in order to follow the lesson.

2. Another predicament related to Andrew's difficulties not knowing when to stop doing something in particular situations. For example, Andrew and some friends were horsing around and somebody said "that's enough" in a sing-song or giggling voice, Andrew would think that they were not seriously calling a halt to the action, and he would continue horsing around. His friends knew when to stop goofing around before getting into trouble, but Andrew could not pick up on these verbal cues and would always go one step too far.

3. Another difficulty he had revolved around his lack of organizational and time management skills. For example, one time he had to speak with a teacher after class about finishing a test he had not completed. Because of this, he did not have time to stop by his locker to get his assignment without risking being late for his next class. So, he went to his next class figuring that once he was in class he would ask the teacher for permission to go to his locker and get his assignment. The problem occurred when the teacher would not let him leave the room and told him that his assignment was now considered late and he would lose points on his grade. Andrew got in trouble because he did not know how to handle such a situation appropriately.

4. Andrew also had periodic difficulties with his peers. Because he tends to be very concrete, kids realize they can easily put something over on him and often picked on him, both verbally and physically. Even though he is small in stature, he could always defend himself due to his Karate training. However, he has always been taught to use Karate only as a last resort if there were no other way to defend himself.

The assistant principal discussed above realized that Andrew was "a good kid" at heart and understood exactly why Andrew would end up in certain predicaments. He worked with Andrew to help him work out his difficulties with his peers as they came up and would speak to his teachers and try to smooth over some of the problems.

This man created an atmosphere in which Andrew felt he could trust him implicitly and an atmosphere in which I felt I could call him and express some of my own concerns. The assistant principal's daughter was a speech-language pathologist, and he had some personal understanding of why Andrew had some of his difficulties. I also felt that he respected me both as a parent and as a professional in the field. After many of our conversations, he would thank me for being involved and for working with him to help Andrew.

Toward the end of Andrew's eighth grade year, the assistant principal said that one of the things that he enjoyed about working with Andrew and me was that we did not use Andrew's disability as an excuse but rather we used it as a way to understand Andrew and we still expected certain behavior and grades from him despite his disability. I felt that he watched out for the best interests of my son and helped him more than his guidance counselor and anyone else in his school career. It should be noted that he also held Andrew accountable for his actions and misdeeds when Andrew needed to take responsibility for them.

High school brought its' own challenges. We continued to have a meeting with all of his teachers at the beginning of every school year. However, his Section 504 renewal meetings were moved to the end of the school year. One of the positive differences that we encountered was that his guidance counselor in the high school was not very only understanding, but she was helpful and looked out for Andrew's best interest. She attended all of the meetings that we had with his teachers in the beginning of the year and his Section 504 meetings that we had in May as well.

There were many times during each of these meetings that his guidance counselor made very helpful suggestions, in terms of Andrew's course selections and when it came time to start thinking about the college he would attend. She would also point out when she felt that we were, for lack of a better word, "babying" Andrew. For example, during one of the Section 504 meetings, at the end of his junior year of school, we started to discuss which book Andrew would pick from the summer reading list. My husband complained that there were no books of interest to Andrew on the list and that he was going to call the assistant superintendent about letting him pick a different book. The guidance counselor pointed out to my husband, that Andrew was one year away from college and that in college he would have to read many books that were not of interest to him. My husband was not happy, but he did realize that she had a good point and backed off.

One of the other problems that we encountered when Andrew was in high school was that he could not have any heavy academic course at the end of the day. By the end of the day, he had auditory fatigue and could not handle having to process a subject like Chemistry. At times it seemed as if his guidance counselor hand picked his schedule. She would schedule one or two academic classes, then a light subject class like gym or art, then a heavy academic class, lunch, heavy academic class and then a light subject. This enabled him to take a breather in between his academic subjects which would help to lessen his auditory overload. In his senior year, he had two free periods every other day which was also very helpful.

The high school handled his accommodations differently than the middle school did. For example, they gave him a second set of books due to his poor organizational skills and we no longer needed to get a doctor's note. In the high school all of the students with Section 504 testing accommodations take their tests in the "504 room," and not with their particular course teacher. At first I was apprehensive because I felt that this would really single him out and draw attention to him. That was not the case. The positive to this change was that he could use his extra time whenever it fit his schedule as opposed to an individual teacher's schedule. The only draw back to this setup is that the section 504 proctor was not usually fully versed in all of the subjects and when she or he would have to paraphrase or restate a question it was sometimes done incorrectly and would then cause Andrew to answer incorrectly. If this tended to happen frequently in a particular subject, Andrew would then work out with the class teacher a plan of taking the test in class and coming back to the teacher during a free period to finish the test.

Andrew's testing accommodations of "separate location" to reduce noise and distractions did not work out well when it came to state tests like the Regents. The school put all of the Section 504 students in the library to take the Regent exams. Now, while this was a separate location from the students taking it in the gym, it was not a "minimal distraction" environment. The proctors tended to talk to each other and they each had walkie talkies that were left on. After his experience with this for the ninth grade Regents, I spoke with the school psychologist and he switched Andrew to small group testing for the state exams. This made a tremendous difference for Andrew in his ability to focus during the test.

Before Andrew left middle school, we asked the assistant principal who had always looked out for Andrew, if there was someone at the high school that Andrew could befriend in the same manner. He made a suggestion, and Andrew sought him out when he got to the high school. This particular assistant principal was helpful to Andrew during his four years in the high school, but I did not have contact with him the way that I had with the middle school assistant principal. Some relationships are difficult to duplicate, and Andrew did not need me to be involved in the same way anymore.

Andrew started to attend different college fairs at the end of his freshman year of high school. At the fairs, he would ask the representatives of the colleges about their Learning Disability programs and how they handled students with testing accommodations. Once he became a Junior in high school we started to seriously look into colleges and the college entrance exams. Andrew's guidance counselor suggested that he take the ACT exams. I had never heard of the ACT exam. She explained that the colleges looked at the ACT test the same wasy that they looked at the SAT test, however, the ACT concentrated more heavily on other academic subjects besides English and Math. Andrew has never done well in group tutoring situations so I resigned myself to the expense of having a one to one tutor to help him prepare for the tests as opposed to one of the study programs that offered weekly classes.

We applied for Andrew to have extended test taking time and separate location accommodations for the SAT and ACT exams. The SAT gave him extended time without a problem (documenting that he had this accommodation previously for several years helped). The ACT required two appeals before he was approved of for the extra time. The separate location or minimal distraction environment was handled by the school in that they assigned Andrew to take the test in a room that only had several students in it.

When Andrew did not come close to breaking 1000 on the SAT test, we decided to concentrate on bringing his score up on the ACT test. Between tutors for the Regent exams, academic subjects like Math and Chemistry, and tutors for the ACT, it seemed like there was always a tutor in my house. At the end of that year, I had spent $6700 on tutoring, which is about $4000 more than I usually spent in a year of tutors. When we went on-line to check for his scores on his second ACT test, I couldn't believe my eyes. He had jumped four points in his total score, which was the equivalent to jumping a few hundred points on the SAT test. We had hoped that he would jump four points (his top two college choices wanted a score of 22 and his previous score was an 18) but we really didn't think that he would be able to pull it off. It's not that we didn't believe in him, but making that type of jump on this test is very difficult to do.

Within two to three weeks of his new ACT score, he received letters from his first two college choices stating that he had been accepted. Andrew applied to six colleges and had been accepted to all six. To help narrow down the colleges that he was applying to, we went on college tours and met with people from the admissions department and from the learning disability programs.

Some colleges offered a learning disabilities program for a fee or having testing accommodations under Section 504 without paying a fee for a program. The differences between the two is that the learning disability programs usually provided: mandatory tutoring every week, coordinating extra time for exams, a counselor or person to help him negotiate difficulties that they would encounter in college (professors don't want to talk to parents) and offered early registration so students could sign up for professors who worked well with learning disabled students. The alternative of just having testing accommodations left all of the coordinating time for taking tests and letting professors know about his accommodations up to him to take care of.

At first, I felt that if Andrew was going to live at home that I didn't need to pay more money to a college for a learning disability program, that we could take care of it ourselves like we had to this point in time. Then his guidance counselor pointed out that his professors would not talk with me because he was over 18 and that I had spent a fortune in tutoring which was included in these programs. But more importantly, she helped my husband and I to realize that if we wanted him to take that next step toward independence, we needed to have him in a learning disability program. The programs involved him being in regular classes, but offered him the supports that he would need.

During Andrew's junior year of high school, the school psychologist said that he would update Andrew's psychological testing. This surprised me because many schools will not do so for Section 504 students because it is not mandated by federal law. I knew that he would need updated testing for when he applied to the learning disability programs in the colleges, so I was happy that he was willing to do so. When I received the report, I saw that he had administered the Woodcock –Johnson Cognitive test, instead of the Wechsler Adult Intelligence Scale. When I questioned him about it, he said that the colleges would accept it. Well, as it turned out they would, but not happily. They really wanted the Wechsler Adult Intelligence Scale and they wanted to see how the Auditory Processing Disorder affected his ability to learn. I ended up having to have him tested privately (insurance companies do not generally cover this), in order to get the report that the learning disability programs were looking for.

During the summer before his senior year of high school we went to speak with the learning disability programs and Section 504 coordinators at several of the colleges that he was interested in. The first interview was an enlightening experience, to put it lightly. I take pride that my son has a full understanding of his APD, understands his Section 504 accommodations and can advocate for himself. Having said that, he could not answer the interviewer's barrage of questions about his APD, how it affected him in school and why he needed testing accommodations. I realized after that first interview that we had to do a lot of preparation before his next interview.

The second interview went much better. This was due in part by my preparing Andrew more for the interview, and also due in part to the person interviewing him. She didn't sit behind a desk to talk to us, instead we sat in a comfortable arrangement of chairs that made the atmosphere much more relaxing than that of the first interview. The director of the program, who was conducting the interview, asked him questions that helped Andrew to relax, such as "What sports are you into?", "What do you enjoy doing when you are not in school?", etc..

These two interviews that I mentioned were just information gathering interviews. When Andrew was called for an admissions interview to the learning disability program at Adelphi University, the person setting up the interview indicated that it would be a one to one interview with Andrew and the assistant director of the program. I was told that I could come along and wait in the waiting room while he had his 20 to 25 minute interview. To say that Andrew and I were a little nervous would have been an understatement. Adelphi University was Andrew's first choice of colleges and if the learning disability program accepted him, it would override any decision that the school's Admission Department would make. In other words, if Adelphi's Admission's Department did not accept him and their Learning Disability Program did, he would still be admitted to the school. So a lot was riding on that interview.

After a half hour had passed and Andrew was still in the interview I started to get a bit nervous. Almost 45 minutes after he went into the interview he came out to get me. On the way back to the interviewer, he said to me "I think she said that I was accepted." I was like, "What do you mean you "think" she said that you were accepted, aren't you sure?" When we walked into the interviewer's office, she related to me as to how impressed she had been with Andrew and that normally she doesn't tell students at the interview if they had been accepted or not, but that she was going to make an exception in his case. Andrew had been accepted into the Learning Disability Program, which meant that he had been accepted to his first choice school. Three days later, we got a letter from the Admissions Department, Andrew had been accepted based on his grades and ACT scores, totally independently of the Learning Disability Program acceptance.

Andrew and I have both experienced difficulties with peer relationships due to the fact that we both tend to be concrete and things like sarcasm go over our heads. As I have grown older, this has become less a problem mainly because of the particular friendships that I have developed. Additionally, when I was in school, I tended to wait after class or during a break to ask teachers questions. This way, I was less embarrassed in front of my peers when my questions were off base. Andrew tends to do the same thing.

One thing on which we have worked very hard with Andrew was to get him to ask for clarification when he is not sure of what someone has said. It was typical for Andrew to use a person's tone of voice and body language to guess the appropriate response by nodding his head in agreement when he had no clue what had been said. For example, if you said in a loud, excited voice, "I want a hug," but said it with a serious face, Andrew would think you were mad.

As I previously mentioned, only a few people could tell by the look on his face when this was taking place. It took a lot of catching him in the act of doing this, combined with a lot of positive praise when he would eventually ask for clarification to break Andrew of this habit. To some degree, he still relies on facial expressions, body language and visual cues to answer questions when he is not sure of what is being asked of him, and he occasionally does not ask for further clarification. However, he does not do this nearly as much as he did in the past.

I respect my son for many reasons, one of them being his courage to give up a major coping mechanism and to learn a new one that involves letting people know that he did not understand what they had just said. I realized a while ago, that I used the same maladaptive coping mechanism of looking for facial expressions and body language at times instead of asking for clarification when I did not know what the person has just said. This is easier and less embarrassing than admitting to someone that I did not understand what they had just said. Now, when I find myself needing more clarification, I remind myself of what we have taught Andrew, and I ask the person to restate what was just said.

Another strategy that I described being successful for me *(see Chapter 5)* has been always carrying a pen and paper. This strategy has been so successful and important in my life, that over the last two years my husband and I have tried to get Andrew to carry a small pad and pen with him at school. Andrew used to write down all of his assignments in his planer/schedule book. However, during the seventh grade, he stopped writing everything in his book and tried relying on his memory. He said that his teachers often added something to the assignments after he had put his planner/schedule book away and he did not have time to start pulling the book out again when the teacher made the last minute changes or additions to the assignments. This quickly became a bad situation with which we had to deal with because Andrew was not bringing home the information he needed to complete his assignments.

After much debate (between Andrew and I), he started keeping a very small notepad in his pocket. This helped to alleviate the problem of forgetting information like assignments. Every so often, he decides that he no longer wants to carry the pad with him and we go through a few days of calling his friends to get the information that he needs.

One problem that has led to him not being able to have the pen and paper available is that I have found it hard to find athletic shorts and t-shirts with pockets that comfortably fit a small pad and pen.

Another problem that affects Andrew because of his APD is that noises barely noticed by most people are like nails scratching on a blackboard for Andrew. For example, we had to remove a wall clock from his bedroom because the ticking of the clock kept him from being able to fall asleep. Recently, we also had to replace a wall clock with a digital clock in our dining room because he could not block out the ticking while working on his homework at the dinning room table.

During the summer, I would often let Andrew miss a day or two of camp when the camp had their "color war" games (i.e., organized competition and a general boot camp environment with screaming, shouting). After his experiences with "color war" at two different camps, I felt that it was not something with which he needed to be "tortured" because all the yelling, shouting and general commotion that goes on during this event was too much for him to handle. It was pure torture for him compared to the enjoyment shared by the other kids.

Some children can go from one activity such as working in school to playing a sports game, having a snack in the car on the way to another sport activity, and then doing homework when they get home. Andrew has always needed a "down-time" period between activities. For example, if he had sports after school, it was difficult for him to go to religious instruction class straight from practice, and then go home and start his homework. Although he has had to do this at times, particularly during the year of his Bar Mitzvah, it is very stressful for him. He would become exhausted and experienced headaches as well as experiencing auditory fatigue on days when he had to endure one activity after another.

I am not a big fan of children sitting in front of the television or playing video games for periods of time. However, this is how Andrew is able to relax and "not think." It is a time particularly when he is playing a video game or watching sports on TV with the sound off that he does not have to process any auditory information.

Andrew is usually the last or second to last person out of the locker room no matter which sport he is playing. He rarely does anything quickly aside from playing a sport. In the house, I usually give him fifteen minutes and five minute interval warnings before he has to leave to go on to a new activity. He has no real sense of time; two minutes can easily turn into one hour with him. If I don't give him the time warnings and I just say, "Let's go," he feels as if someone has pulled the rug out from under him a very unsettling feeling.

Over the years, Andrew has learned to self-advocate for himself. If a teacher does not follow his Section 504 accommodations, he will inform the teacher about them. Sometimes it is cleared up at that point and the teacher corrects what he or she has not been providing as an accommodation. When a teacher refuses to offer him one of his accommodations, he informs them that one of his parents will be in touch with them. Andrew knows that it would be disrespectful to get into an argument with a teacher. He then comes home and informs me what took place and what needs to be corrected.

It has taken many years to get Andrew to this point of being able to self-advocate. I feel that it is important for children to learn how to self-advocate because parents cannot be with them all the time and teachers do not always follow through on what they are supposed to do.

I hope that my Andrew continues to grow into a self confident adult and that he finds his APD to be nothing more than a part of him with which he can cope with successfully. And, unlike myself *(see Chapter 5)* and my father before me *(see Chapter 4)*, I hope that Andrew has many positive experiences in spite of his APD and finds it easier to deal with living with APD now that more and more people learning about processing disorders and accepting them.

Chapter Eight

Carmela Granata Bernacchio and
Danielle Carmela Lisanti:
A Mother and Daughter's view of life
with Auditory Processing Disorders
by Carmela Granata Bernacchio

(Note from Dr. J: Carmela is a speech-language pathologist who provides treatment for children and adults with APD. She is an associate with Dr. J, and provided APD treatment for Andrew. Carmela is also the mother of two daughters who have APD. These are Carmela's words, edited by Dr. J, explaining a mother's feelings and struggles to help her daughters with APD. The last part of this chapter presents the words of one of Carmela's daughters explaining her personal struggle overcoming APD.)

Carmela's Story

I can still remember where I was when I realized that my daughter Danielle had a problem. It was a problem different from any other I had ever known as a teacher, a speech/language pathologist, a member of a big Italian family or as a child, myself. She was only 18 months old, but I could see that something kept her from connecting to the rest of the world. If I were in close proximity to her, she understood and responded. Yet, when I spoke from a distance or when we were in social setting she was aloof and confused.

From the moment of my realization that my daughter had a problem, to the moment of my taking action, years passed. I was in complete shock! How was I to find the solution to the problem when I didn't even know what the problem was? I think back now and realize that even with my background working with children, I needed

105

a great deal of help in identifying my own daughter's problems and even more help in addressing them. I often wonder, how can parents who have no prior experiences with children who have APD recognize their own children's problems?

I did not truly understand Danielle's difficulties when she first entered school. At that time, her teachers called her everything from shy to autistic. Some even described her as flaky. They wondered why she spent so much time with the boys and so little time with the girls. Ask her now and she would say, "I kept up with the boy's limited conversations and games better. The girls were too chatty."

Teachers also described her as high strung, sensitive to sound, impulsive, and sometimes rude. But she wasn't rude. She was trying to grab hold of the conversation so she didn't have to process new information. Without resources for an accurate diagnosis and with teachers who did not understand, I decided to pull her out of mainstream schooling where I feared she would fail and have her self-esteem destroyed.

I found a school that was better suited for her needs. It used visual cues, repetition and demonstration as a focus in its teaching. It allowed a child to learn at a pace comfortable to the child.

"We played all kinds of games and did many types of arts and crafts and learned through play. I was unaware that all the play was turning into information and knowledge," Danielle later tells me reflecting on her early education experiences at this school. The minimal focus of teaching through "words" assisted her learning.

At home, I taught Danielle every way I could. I read everything I could find, and since I sensed that the problem was connected to her hearing, I began to research the connection between sound and language. I found information on Alfred Tomatis. Enthralled, I became possessed. I hired tutors and a speech-language pathologist who would accept my guidance and work with my daughter on the goals I prescribed. Much of the therapy dealt with learning how to listen and how to pay attention.

I did a great deal myself. Danielle and I fought every night and through the screaming, I taught her to read. Next, I bought a transcriber from a professional store that sold secretarial supplies and used it to slow down speech. This enabled Danielle to learn how to listen to oral directives and to find key words. I also used the transcriber to teach her how to build her phonological awareness skills as I broke up words into single phonemes and blended them together from a sequence of individual sounds.

Danielle was able to hear this process slowly, and as she improved I sped up the tape. She could speak into the device, play it back to herself at "her best processing rate," and produce written work free from her usual struggles with spelling, handwriting, etc.

When Danielle switched from this school environment to a mainstream setting, she prepared for class before time, sat in the front of the room, and asked lots and lots of questions. I taught her that if she didn't hear what was said she should ask for clarification and repeat back to the teacher what she heard. She was willing to do that. With a little help from me she was able to succeed. It was a challenge for both of us but I felt that we had conquered her Auditory Processing Disorders (APD). I soon found that there was more I needed to learn.

After Danielle was born, I had a son, Paul Adam, and then another daughter, Lauren, my youngest. I also got a wake up call. As a little girl, Lauren liked to take walks. But, when she walked, she walked a few steps behind. Independent and in charge, she resigned herself to a secondary position for fear of not fitting in.

While her friends gabbed about life and learned valuable lessons, Lauren remained isolated, spending her time trying to decipher the strange language her friends used. She recognized the sounds and some of the words, but she did not recognize what they were saying. The meaning of the words eluded her. So, to play it safe, Lauren walked a few steps behind her friends, but mostly she walked alone.

Here I was, again, with a daughter with a problem that very few understood, but this time I was ready. Or was I? Though the two girls had similarities in their disabilities, there were many striking differences. At the time I started to deal with Lauren's problems, I was directing a preschool. I wrote the curriculum and followed much of the same philosophy of the school Danielle had attended. Lauren attended the pre-school at which I was the director. This helped Lauren obtain success until she entered first grade. Unlike Danielle, she did not attend private school until fifth grade. I was not able to afford it.

When Lauren was ready for kindergarten, I enrolled her in the public school and watched her regress, lose her self-esteem and become withdrawn, moody and sad. For Lauren, life as a child was life spent in a corner as the object of laughter or at least that's how she saw it. Desperately searching for social connections and meeting obstacle after obstacle, she stopped trying. She couldn't express herself because she didn't know how or when to speak up. She didn't understand why what she said led to blank stares or laughter that she learned to dread.

In addition to problems communicating with others, the general noises of the world threatened to drown her in sound. Loud noises were scary and soft noises were indecipherable. People who found the right tone couldn't find the right words and Lauren was lost. I met a lot of resistance trying to convince her teachers of the severity of her situation. It was not until an incident in third grade, when Lauren fell to the floor during gym holding her ears and crying, that a teacher agreed that I might have a point. The principal called me and said, "We have to talk about Lauren." I knew that meant that Lauren was being considered for special education.

Despite the evidence of her behaviors, she was labeled as inattentive and was demanded to focus and pay attention. Lauren did not know what was wrong. Her frustration in the misdiagnosis of an attention disorder as well as the fact that no one could help her led to her further withdrawing from the world around her. Afraid, and now fatigued, she hid in the protective atmosphere of her family.

When she was formally assessed, it was found that she had significant auditory processing deficits (APD). At this point, the only way I could save her was to take her out of the public schools and home school her. So with a new set of tools, I tackled the new face of APD.

With Lauren "attached to my hip," I pushed the academics to the side and attacked the underlying problem. I purchased and mastered computer programs like Earobics and Fast Forword. These programs are designed to exercise auditory skills such as memory, integration, and phonemic synthesis. In my own learning center, I created a schedule of one-on-one tutors to administer programs like the reading programs "Open Court" and "Junior Reading" to bridge the gap between Lauren's potential and academic achievement.

When she was ready, I found a school with a small student population and a positive outlook on life. It was there that Lauren reintegrated herself into the world of classic academics, eventually going on to high school.

All the while, I was interested in keeping her active to make friends. She particularly took to sports or more accurately to the way in which coaches taught sports: through demonstration. Any confounding words were removed from the equation, and Lauren learned through watching and through physical repetition of the process. She developed a love for riding horses, basketball, soccer, and track.

Lauren explained to me that the primary difference between herself as a child and the young woman she is now could be measured by her self-esteem. She admits to being able to translate the English language better, but it is her self-confidence that allows her to ask questions that improve her understanding or try new things even though she is not an expert. To achieve an audience with Lauren now, you have to catch her between one of her many practices and her chatting with friends or one of her teammates. When first asked to describe herself, Lauren triumphantly lists: funny, outgoing, cute, and having a pretty smile. "You said just be honest. Admit it, I have a pretty smile," she says to me.

In that respect, Danielle is no different. From being a shy little girl, she is now an outgoing young woman. She is forthright and expressive, friendly and understanding.

"When I see myself being successful in the world I know that I am having a different experience than at school," Danielle admits.

"When I was at school, I wasn't 'right.' It feels good to actually be 'right' and see that I am good at something and that I can make a difference in people's lives." Danielle is currently teaching children with special needs including those with APD.

So how did two painfully shy little girls who even now are still shackled by the restraints of APD not only blossom, but burst into independence? Through knowledge, determination and ultimately understanding, which was all they wanted in the first place.

Danielle: In Her Own Words

(Note: In preparing this chapter, Carmela asked her daughters to provide input in their own words. Danielle was willing to do so by responding to specific questions. Danielle was in college at the time these questions were asked and she responded. The following are the questions and her responses edited by Dr.J.)

What do you remember of yourself as a child in elementary school?

It's hard to remember myself as a child. I was always very quiet around people that I didn't know. I had only one really good friend who lived on my block, or I was always with my cousins. I ran around the playground with the boys at school, but I don't remember much about being with the girls or whether I played with them. If I did, it would only have been inside.

I preferred the boys. Somehow I was better able to keep up with their conversations. The girls were too chatty. When I look back, I feel like I only stayed with the girls inside because it was quiet and outside it was too loud.

I was always close with my teachers and I loved playing with them. I have very clear memories of my teachers. The nursery and kindergarten teachers at Waldorf were my favorites. The quiet and structured atmosphere and their "soft" way of interacting comforted me. *(Note: Waldorf was a private school Danielle attended.)*

What was the best thing about you as a child?

The best thing about being a child was when I went to school for six years from nursery to fourth grade. I went to a nontraditional school called Waldorf. I was able to learn through play. I was unaware that all the play was turning into information and knowledge. But looking back, I understand. We played all types of games and did many types of arts and crafts projects, and learned through our experiences involved with the process.

Being at home was always comfortable and fun. I loved being with my cousins and aunts. Part of the reason I didn't have so many friends was that I was constantly with my cousins.

What was the worst thing you can remember from your childhood education?

I don't remember the worst thing because my mom sheltered me at Waldorf. I never felt out of place there because there wasn't anything I couldn't do. It was always play time, therefore, I was successful.

At home, working on reading with my mom was bad! I still don't know how we ever got through it. We fought every night. Through all that fighting, I don't understand how I learned to read. Yet, she used the method that I now teach in our center. I teach this method because I "feel" the process. I guess somehow it got through to me, but I hated that my mother taught me because she taught me "behind closed doors" as she "hid" me in Waldorf School.

The process of learning to read was slower for me then for other kids. When I got into the third grade, I was somewhat nervous because I knew the rest of my class was reading and I wasn't. So, I worked every night with mom on reading. It was so hard with a lot of screaming. I don't know how we ever got through. Somehow, through all the screaming, I learned how to read. Although my confidence in school improved, I could read to my teachers but never around other children. I got too nervous.

Describe yourself now.

From being a shy little girl, I became a very outgoing young woman. When I was younger, I couldn't talk to new people. Today, I have no problem stepping right up and expressing myself. I feel confident most times, and get more confident as I get older, especially when I succeed at work and in other areas. I feel better at work when someone thinks that the advice I give is valid and helpful.

When I was at school, I wasn't "right." Teachers didn't always grade me well and today, it feels good to actually be "right" and see that I am good at something and can make a difference in people's lives.

I have felt this confidence since I graduated from college because I see success in myself everyday, and I am not always hitting a brick wall. However, there are times when I doubt myself, when I feel like I am right but second-guess myself. People who try to "push their knowledge" or act "academically arrogant" throw me off center. It takes me a while to build myself up again around such people.

I am learning more about my skills and myself. I find that people who are book smart many times have a harder time in some ways to connect with other people and apply themselves to real life situations. Their successes in school don't always translate to success in the everyday world. I feel that because I have learned social skills, learning strategies, and how to interact in situations, I am better at many daily life skills than these "book smart" people. I can function better at work and with other people compared with them. I am good at every day life situations.

What's the best thing about you now?

I am a friendly and understanding person and can relate to people more then others because of my experiences. I did a lot of observing when I was growing up. I was afraid to say things because I didn't want to be wrong and feel stupid. Now, I feel I can understand a lot more about people and help them.

What's the toughest thing about communicating with people?

I don't always know how to explain myself. I can't always find the words to explain what I am feeling or to tell people how to do something. I am now aware of my integration and organization problems, and I understand why I "observed" and didn't speak up as a child. Now, I try to provide myself with information before I speak. Then, when I do speak, I can express myself accurately. Sometimes I have to talk myself into having patience.

What was the toughest thing about learning for you?

Dealing with the teachers! If a teacher happened to teach the way I learned, it was easy for me. But when teachers taught in an opposing style, it was very hard for me. I am an extremely visual person, and I need lots of notes and examples. Especially, real life examples! When I had a teacher who didn't provide a lot of notes on the board I was lost. If the subject was something to which I could not relate, I was also lost. If I could relate to the subject and had lots of visuals, I had less trouble taking in and understanding the information.

Describe school for you as a student.

I always needed to be sitting in the front row. If I were too far back in the room I didn't hear things and missed information. When I was up front, I was able to stay focused and had less trouble understanding.

I always got frustrated watching friends doing better then me, especially since I was studying twice as hard. I hated that everything came easy to them. In high school, it was difficult because a lot of my friends were in honors classes, and I was in standard classes. It bothered me the most in college because there were times when I really wanted to go out but I couldn't because I needed to study. I developed many tricks to help me study and stay focused. In class, I sat up front. It was ironic when I was alone studying. When in class, I needed it to be very quiet. Yet, when I studied, I need a little noise in the room. If it was too quiet, I got distracted.

I am still very nervous about reading in front of people. I can't do it. There are very few people in my life in front of whom I feel comfortable reading aloud. I get too nervous and forget words. This is my biggest fear right now. I let my nerves get to me and I get embarrassed.

Describe school for you as a teacher.

Being a teacher is fun because I can apply everything I learned to my job. I also am continuing my education by taking classes in which I am interested and those that apply to the kids with whom I am working. I learn new techniques to use with these kids. Learning now is freedom for me.

What compelled you to work with children?

That is difficult to explain because I don't know what is inside that compels me to want to help children. I love working with children on the autistic spectrum. I see things in them that I feel are very special. I tried to fight my natural tendency to work with children because I felt I was doing it only because of my mom. But no matter how hard I tried, I couldn't stay away.

Every day is different when I work with these children with special needs, and I have to stay on my toes and be creative. It's challenging to work with children on the spectrum but when I see success, the reward is 100 times better then being a regular education teacher. I tend to gravitate to children with language and behavior problems. I feel I connect more with them than with children who have other needs.

What do you think is special in what you offer to children with special needs?

It's hard to explain. Because of what I went through, I think it gave me more patience to review concepts over and over again. Also, I have years of experience because ever since I can remember I was helping my mother in her sessions with children who had learning problems such as APD.

114

What do you understand is APD?

When your brain is always processing the sentence in the past and not the sentence in the present, this is APD to me.

What do think you understand about APD that others may not?

I learned ways to deal with APD, successful ways I dealt with my own problems. I want to teach those ways to others.

What helped you with overcome your APD?

The tricks I developed along the way, such as sitting in the front of room, which helped me to be less distracted and able to hear the teacher more clearly. My mother wanted me to participate in some auditory training programs that became available when I was already a college student. By then, I was used to my tricks and didn't need those training programs. However, I think they help children before they learn tricks to get around their APD.

What else would you like to add?

I overcame my APD and others can do so, too. There are many new programs available, and people are really starting to understand the problems children have with APD. But, what children need to learn most is to become self-confident and realize they can overcome problems with learning.

Chapter Nine

Diagnosis of
Auditory Processing Disorders

by Jay R. Lucker Ed.D., CCC-A/SLP, FAAA

Parents, educators, and other professionals are concerned when they find a child they feel may have an auditory information processing disorder (APD). This chapter focuses on symptoms and testing for APD in general, not the specific tests used. This chapter also discusses who does the testing, how it is done, and an overview of the general areas assessed in comprehensive APD testing. The chapter will also discuss the APD testing and results for Loraine and Andrew so the readers can reflect on how their APD test findings go along with the problems/symptoms these people discuss in their respective chapters.

How do you know whether the problems you have or you see in your child are due to deficits in auditory information processing or due to some other issue? How do you find out whether the auditory information processing deficits (APD) noted are due to primary auditory problems, cognitive problems, behavioral-emotional issues, language problems or sensory-regulatory difficulties? The answer is to get a comprehensive, differential diagnosis. This chapter discusses what behaviors you may see and how they may relate to the five different systems involved in auditory information processing. Additionally, this chapter discusses what is involved in the various assessments with a focus on the auditory based assessments used. In order to help the reader understand the auditory assessment for APD, a discussion of such assessments for Loraine, and Andrew is provided that describes their actual APD test findings and how this author interpreted the findings to identify the specific categories of APD for each of them.

As described earlier in this book *(see Chapter Two)*, auditory information processing is viewed by this author as involving the comprehensive integrative functions of five basic systems. Thus, the first step in assessment is to identify what specific systems may be the underlying factors accounting for the behaviors presented by you or your child when having difficulties processing auditory information. For example, a person can have problems processing verbal messages because that person has difficulties maintaining focal attention (behavioral-emotional system). However, the problems could be due to a deficit with sensory regulation so that the child, for example, cannot use the sensory information appropriately and is not aware of its importance and the need to maintain attention. Another possible cause could be an inability to comprehend the language used so that the message is misinterpreted and, thus, the listener stops attending because he/she cannot follow the meaning of the words spoken (a language system problem). Of course, the problem could be some area of auditory based processing such as being unable to pull out the key auditory features that differentiate one phoneme from another leading to problems discriminating which words are being spoken so the message becomes misinterpreted (an auditory system problem).

In the ideal world, every person identified as having problems understanding auditory information should receive an assessment of all five systems. Therefore, let us deal with the ideal world and then look at what occurs in the real world. Deficits involving the auditory system fall under the scope of practice of the audiologists. An audiologist is a professional who deals with disorders of the auditory system having to do with hearing and processing of information via the auditory system. Audiologists are trained at the professional doctorate level and, today, hold a doctoral level degree (AuD, PhD, EdD, or DSc) in audiology. Audiologists have completed the clinical requirements for certification as an audiologist and may hold the Certificate of Clinical Competence from the American Speech-Language-Hearing Association (ASHA) in Audiology (CCC-A) or Board Certification in Audiology from the American Board of Examiners in Audiology, part of the American Academy of Audiology. In most states, audiologists must also hold state licensure as an audiologist in that state in order to provide services in that state.

Some, not all, audiologists have training and experience in assessing auditory based processing as part of the APD assessment. For many audiologists, assessment for APD is merely the administration of and scoring of tests to identify if a child passes or fails the tests. Additionally, many professionals in the field of APD feel that only audiologists can assess APD issues. They do not understand the need or importance of a team approach because they view APD as only an auditory system disorder. This is not the recommendation of this author. However, the diagnosis of APD is described as falling solely under the scope of practice of the audiologist by the ASHA in their report regarding the audiologist's role in assessment of children with APD as well as implied in their Technical Report on APD (ASHA, 2005a & b).

The team needed to assess a child for an auditory information processing deficit needs to include a team that will look at each of the five systems identified as contributing to the processing of auditory information *(see Chapter Two for further discussion of these five systems)*.

The psychologist is the professional who is trained and experienced in assessing the cognitive and behavioral-emotional systems. Psychologists may work in schools and be known as school psychologists or outside the school setting and be known as clinical psychologists. Some psychologists go further in their post graduate, doctoral level training, to become neuropsychologists, although many clinical psychologists also provide neuropsychological assessments. Psychologists in schools may hold either a graduate (master's) degree such as an M.A., M.S., M.Ed., or a doctoral degree such as a Psy.D., Ph.D. or Ed.D. However, psychologists working outside of schools traditionally hold only a doctoral degree as most state licensing boards that regulate and license psychologists require that such professionals hold a doctorate degree.

Psychologists traditionally do cognitive testing such as IQ testing. For people with APD, it is often important that the cognitive testing not be biased by language, and psychologists can administer non-verbal IQ tests such as the Test of Non-verbal Intelligence (TONI), the Comprehensive TONI (C-TONI), or the Universal Non-verbal Intelligence Test (UNIT) among other non-verbal IQ tests. Psychologists also can provide evaluations of academic functioning using achievement tests such as the Woodcock-Johnson Test, Third Edition, Achievement (WJ-III-ACH), the Wechsler Individual Achievement Test (WIAT), or the Wide Range Achievement Test (WRAT) among others. Additionally, psychologists can provide assessments of behavior using checklists as well as projective tests. What is important to note is that not all psychologists understand or are experienced to assess people with a specific focus on the fact that these people may have APD. Thus, many people with APD receive psychological assessments that have not taken into account how their processing difficulties could affect the cognitive and educational test findings. In some cases, people with primary APD problems are identified as being cognitively impaired when it is the auditory, language, or sensory-regulatory problems that account for the person's difficulties on psychological and educational achievement tests.

Language testing is typically part of the psychologist's assessment. However, psychologists have limited training and experience dealing with language developmental issues and disorders. They view language from a psychological developmental and disorder perspective. In contrast, speech-language pathologists are the professionals whose training, education, experiences and scope of practice focuses on language acquisition, development, and disorders. Thus, it is the speech-language pathologist who typically provides the assessment of the language issues that may be related to APD. Just as described with audiologists and psychologists, many speech-language pathologists do not understand auditory processing and how language participates in APD but is not the total factor accounting for APD.

Speech-language pathologists must hold a minimum of a graduate (master's) degree and clinical training sufficient for clinical certification. Many hold the Certificate of Clinical Competence from

ASHA in speech-language pathology (CCC-SLP). Those working in schools may hold state licensure in speech-language pathology, although in many states, school based speech-language pathologists do not have to be licensed. However, outside of schools and in most non-educational agencies, speech-language pathologists must hold state licensure to work. Many states certify speech-language pathologists who work in the schools.

The idea that school based speech-language pathologists do not have to hold state licensure or ASHA certification leads to a confusion with many parents and even professionals within and outside of schools. Many school districts are allowed to have speech teachers who merely hold a bachelor's degree and do not have the graduate training or clinical experiences needed for certification or state licensing. Thus, many school based speech-language personnel are not speech-language pathologists because they lack the requirements, training, and education. It is necessary for you, the parent, to be sure that the professional in school working with your child who has APD is an appropriately trained professional. You may want to check whether the speech teacher is a speech-language pathologist. Note that only those professionals holding graduate level education and clinical training have the qualifications to apply for certification and, when appropriate, for state licensure, can call themselves speech-language pathologists. In many states, only professionals holding the CCC-SLP or the appropriate state licensing in speech-language pathology can call themselves speech-language pathologists or even just speech pathologists (an older term still in use in many places).

Speech-language pathologists assess various aspects of communication. In the assessment for APD, the speech-language pathologist's role is to assess the language knowledge and language processing abilities of people who have difficulties processing auditory information. Some of the tests they use include receptive and expressive vocabulary tests, batteries of clinical tests of language abilities, and tests assessing some of the ASHA identified skills involved with APD, such as auditory discrimination and auditory memory. What is important to remember is that auditory processing has nothing to do with expressive language as it involves taking in information through the auditory system and making sense out of that information for comprehension. Thus, the focus of the language assessment would be on receptive abilities.

The last system to be checked out is the sensory-regulatory system. The professional whose scope of practice focuses on sensory systems is the occupational therapist or OT. OTs may only hold bachelor level education or graduate (master's) degrees as the requirements for practicing as an OT vary from state to state. Not all OTs are trained in or experienced in assessing and working with people with primary sensory-regulatory problems often referred to as sensory integration disorders (SID). Additionally, not all OTs understand auditory processing and many think that SID in the auditory area is the primary or only aspect of auditory processing needing to be assessed.

It is hoped that the reader understands that the assessment for APD under ideal conditions is comprehensive, involves a multidisciplinary team approach, and can be costly and time consuming. It is most likely that the last two factors (cost and time) have led to what typically occurs in the real world. What happens is that the child does not obtain a comprehensive assessment from all four professionals looking at all five systems, or the four professionals do not make up a multidisciplinary team so problems occur in identifying whether the child is eligible for services through IDEA and Section 504 *(see Chapter two for further discussion of the IDEA and Section 504)*. Additionally, the different professionals may meet with each professional having a differing view as to what is auditory processing and how to assess and identify the presence of APDs.

In the real world, professionals have to triage the individual case determining how to proceed using factors such as the presenting symptoms, case history data, and other reports, or they may use checklists or inventories to determine what systems appear to be at the heart of the individual's auditory processing problems. These professionals then determine which evaluations should be done and which professionals will be seeing the child for assessment. This is typically the case in public school systems.

The schools typically have school psychologists and school based speech-language professionals working for them. Many school psychologists have good clinical training and are able to provide appropriate assessments of children with APD including looking at behavioral issues as well as administering non-verbal IQ tests. Many school speech-language professionals are speech-language pathologists who can provide appropriate, comprehensive language knowledge and language processing assessments. However, in many schools, the psychologists merely perform basic IQ and achievement tests, or the achievement tests are administered by educational evaluators who are not psychologists. Additionally, many speech-language pathologists focus on expressive language issues and do not truly understand receptive language and the involvement of auditory processing in taking in and comprehending verbal messages.

As the reader can see, the above paragraph has left out two of the important professionals in the assessment of APD, the audiologist and the OT. The reason is that most schools do not have audiologists or OTs as part of the staff. Thus, these schools depend on the school psychologist and speech-language professional to perform all the testing for assessing children with APD. In some cases, the schools may refer outside for audiological and OT assessments, but only when the other school professionals, typically not educated in understanding the audiological and sensory-regulatory components of APD, to recommend whether a child needs an audiological or OT evaluation. Then, the professionals to whom these schools refer may not understand what is appropriately needed in assessing the aspects of APD in children they need to assess or they do not have the understanding or experiences of the educational system to deal successfully in providing input to the schools.

This may seem to present a bleak view of how children in schools get assessed for APD. However, it is the real world. Then, what are parents to do? The answer is to seek out professionals who you feel are qualified and can provide the assessments you want and need for your child. This may mean traveling some distance for the assessment, but remember, once the appropriate assessment is completed and the team works together, the identification of the true, underlying factors accounting for the APD can be identified and appropriate, individualized accommodations and treatment can be provided for your child. Additionally, all persons working with the child, including teachers and parents, can have a better understanding of what they need to do to help the child both through providing accommodations and offering instruction and support.

Audiological Assessment of APD

To better understand what professionals do when assessing APD from the psychological, speech-language pathology, and OT perspective, the reader would best look into books written by professionals from those professions. Since the focus of this book has been on the auditory issues involved with APD, the following is an overview of what is involved in the audiological assessment of APD and why such assessments are needed in diagnosing the specific areas of APD.

APD involves the processing of auditory information. To assess this processing, we need to assess the auditory system and control for other confounding variables. The psychological, speech-language, and OT assessments all focus on assessing aspects of information processing: cognitive information, attention, memory, language, and sensory information. But, these assessments do not control for the auditory variables when using auditory based information in their testing. Thus, we need the audiologist who can assess the most important component of auditory processing, the auditory aspects of processing.

The auditory signal contains essentially three factors known as intensity, frequency, and the temporal components of sound. Intensity is related to loudness or volume. One problem in psychological, speech-language, and OT assessments is that these professionals, and their assessment tools, do not control for the volume at which the information is presented to the listener. Thus, even if recorded speech is used, as is done by some psychologists and speech-language pathologists, these professionals set the volume level for listening at some arbitrary value. In contrast, audiologists have sound calibrated equipment that sets the intensity level at a specific dB level. Thus, tests used in the APD assessment are set at a specific intensity level and that level is maintained the same throughout the testing. In the author's practice, the intensity level is typically set at 50dBHL or 70dBSPL (these are the same values in two different scales). Thus, the audiological testing controls for the intensity level at which the listener hears the test information. Additionally, since the intensity level is not changed and the test material is pre-recorded, the variations in intensity remain the same for each and every person taking the same test. In contrast, one wonders whether the psychologist, speech-language pathologist and the OT maintain a constant intensity throughout their testing for one person and whether the same volume level is used when testing other people on the same tests.

The second aspect of the auditory signal is frequency. Frequency is related to pitch (e.g., high, low, or middle pitched). If a male psychologist and a female speech-language pathologist present tests live voice (i.e., spoken) to a listener in their evaluations, and if both performed tests that had a similar focus, such as vocabulary, it is possible that the male voice was clearer and easier for one person to hear compared with the female voice leading to the person passing the vocabulary test administered by the male psychologist, but failing the vocabulary test administered by the female speech-language pathologist. In contrast, all of the audiological tests used are pre-recorded so that the pitch of voice remains constant for the same tests for all clients taking that test.

The last aspect of the auditory signal is called the temporal component. Temporal relates to time, and there are two aspects of time in the auditory system. When considering verbal messages, time relates to the speed at which the information is presented or spoken. When psychologists, speech-language pathologists, and OTs speak to people during testing, one question arises whether they maintain the same rate of speaking throughout their testing. In presenting seminars all over the U.S., this professional has posed this question to audiences of hundreds of people. The overwhelming response from participants is that they are aware that they probably change the speed of their speaking to children when the child responds slower than normal or seems to do better when the speaker is speaking slowly. Yet, these same professionals admitting to doing this change in their rate of speaking admit they often forget to include this information in their reports regarding how the child performed during their testing. In contrast, the audiological tests of APD are all pre-recorded and the rate of speaking remains constant for all presentations of the same test to all people to whom the test is administered.

The second part of the temporal component relates to a factor we may call the stress and rhythm of speech or what language professionals refer to as prosody. People with different accents coming from different cultural backgrounds often have different rhythms to their speaking even if they are all speaking English. Consider the person coming from the northeastern U.S. People in, say, New York City (NYC) often speak much faster than most people in other parts of the country. How about a person coming from what we often refer to as the "deep south." People in this area often speak much slower than and have a very different rhythm to their speech than the person from New York City. Again, the audiological tests of APD are prerecorded so the speaker is the same for the administration of the specific tests being used.

Aside from the auditory components being controlled in audiological tests for APD, language is another component that is not controlled on verbal psychological tests and test for language assessment. That is, when psychologists and speech-language pathologists evaluate a child using verbal material, they do not assess whether the child understands the words being used on the test. For example, on one cognitive IQ test, a child is asked to describe why two things are the same. Thus, a child may be asked, "Why is an orange and a plum the same?" The best answer is that they are both fruit, although an acceptable answer is that you eat them both. However, what if a child has never encountered a plum, and does not know this vocabulary item. Or imagine if the child's only experiences with the plum is that it is purple, but the child is never told just what is a plum. The child might say, "They're not the same, they're different colors." In the second case, the psychologist giving the IQ test might assume the child cannot make the appropriate comparisons by group. Yet, the child has learned to compare the orange and plum by the color (hence a group or categorical distinction) and know that orange and purple (both being colors) are not the same colors, so the child's response is appropriate and related to his/her only experiences with these items.

In contrast to the numerous variables that can affect the outcome of psychological and speech-language tests as well as OT tests involving verbal tasks, the audiological tests of APD have the child primarily repeat words or simple sentences whether the child understands the words or sentences. Thus, understanding the meaning of the words used is not critical to passing the audiological tests of APD. These tests merely ask the child to repeat the words or sentences heard. Only a few audiological tests of APD ask the child to manipulate what has been heard in some manner, and the manipulation is trained before the actual assessment of the skill is made. Furthermore, the manipulation remains the same throughout the test.

What Do The Audiological Tests of APD Involve?

The audiological tests of APD involve the listener to first be assessed for hearing. People having hearing loss could have problems in processing auditory information merely because they can't hear the sounds and words. Thus, some assessment to rule out hearing loss is first accomplished. Then, the child is asked to do the following.

The child is asked to repeat words or sentences for most of the audiological tests. The words are presented sometimes in the presence of background noises that can vary from speech babble (also known as cafeteria noise) to a person saying another sentence or telling a story. Sometimes the words have been electronically distorted such as by filtering or distorted in time such as using computerized speeded up or time compressed speech.

Some tests of auditory processing involve the use of what is called dichotic listening. Dichotic listening tests present a specific test item to one ear and another, similar test item to the opposite ear simultaneously. For example, imagine hearing the word "are" in the right ear and "cow" in the left ear at the same time. If you were asked to repeat all of the words you heard, you could respond, "are, cow," or "cow, are" and you would be correct. However, you might only be able to repeat "are" from the right ear, or "cow" from the left ear, or you might "smush" the two words together and respond with "car." These errors would be counted as errors, but also would be reviewed as to the type of error (example, child repeated items only from the right (or left) ear, or most errors were smushes). Thus, the appropriate analysis of audiological tests of APD take into account the number of errors and the type of errors made. It is largely through this dichotomous analysis (called a quantitative and qualitative) analysis that those professionals holding to a categorical view of APD analyze and interpret the audiological tests of APD.

Some other audiological tests of APD use non-verbal materials. For the two examples provided below, the non-verbal test used was the Pitch Patterns Sequence Test (PPST). This test presents high and low pitched sounds and the listener is asked to label the pattern (first two tones then three tones) as being high-low, low-high, high-high, or low-low (examples for the two tone patterns). If the child performs appropriately for two tone patterns, the actual test using three tone patterns is administered and scored. This is an important component of auditory processing as Lucker (2005a, 2007a, 2008) has described auditory processing as auditory pattern recognition and discrimination. A similar description of auditory processing is included with the ASHA Technical Report (2005).

The last test of auditory processing used in the assessments for the two examples presented below is a test that helps differentiate people with auditory processing problems from those who may have APD due to primary attention deficits such as AD/HD. This is a test of auditory vigilance (ACPT). This test requires the listener to indicate when a target word ("dog") is heard and only when that target word is heard. Errors of omission (not responding when "dog" is presented) and errors of commission (responding to a non-target word such as "teach") are counted for each "trial" or presentation of the list of 96 words. Six trials are presented and performance is viewed across trials. Attention difficulties are picked up as a high level of errors and problems sustaining attention across trials. Children with auditory processing problems not due to primary attention deficits find this task boring, but easy.

Performance for Loraine on the Audiological Part of the APD Testing

Loraine initially came because her son, Andrew, had been having problems in school and was seen for APD testing including audiological tests of APD. The outcome from those tests led Loraine to wonder whether she, too, had APD, and whether her APD was passed down to her son. Reading Loraine's chapter in this book *(see Chapter Five)* demonstrates that her descriptions of problems she had dealing with verbal information spoken to her in school and socially would coincide with a description of a person who has some problems processing auditory information, i.e., APD. However, when Loraine was young, there were no tests for APD being used with children, and as she grew older, she merely lived with her APD never having a reason to get an evaluation, until her son was tested.

Loraine (as with Andrew) was administered a comprehensive audiological/APD assessment including: the SSW Test, the Phonemic Synthesis Test (PST), the Pitch Pattern Sequence Test (PPST), a test of speech understanding in noise using two different noise conditions (The LAD Test, presently an experimental test of auditory processing developed by Lucker), and the Auditory Continuous Performance Test (ACPT). Although this is not as comprehensive a test battery as may be done for other people, such as for her son Andrew, it is sufficient to assess the various categories of APD in Lucker's model.

Loraine was found to have normal hearing. Her SSW scores demonstrated no problems with dichotic listening and no concerns with what are called response biases. No issues related to auditory lexical extraction, memory, organization, sound-symbol association, or with attention issues were identified on the SSW. Her PST performance was very normal for an adult indicating no problems with auditory phonemic extraction and integration (thus, no auditory phonemic awareness deficits). However, problems were found on the PPST.

This test of tonal pattern recognition presented great difficulties for Loraine. She was not able to do the two tone patterns well scoring only 70% correct. Although the three tone patterns are usually not then administered, being an adult, it was decided to go ahead and do that task. Loraine was only able to correctly identify 65% of the three tone patterns when the norm for adults is 75%. (It should be noted that adults without problems in tone pattern recognition and processing obtain 100% for the two tone patterns). Thus, auditory pattern recognition is a problem for Loraine suggesting deficits in temporal processing. When asked about her listening difficulties, Loraine said she often found that people spoke too quickly for her to understand and she needed to carry paper and pencil around with her to insure that she understood and remembered what people told her.

Also found to be problematic were Loraine's abilities to understand speech in the presence of noise. The LAD Test is an experimental test that has preliminary norms for children. On the initial trials with the LAD, adults were found to have little difficulties on the test, and they all performed better than the norms for children. When developing the preliminary norms, only children up to 2nd grade were used as it was found that children from 2nd grade and above were all performing the same. Thus, it was based on these norms that Loraine's performance was compared.

Considering Loraine being an adult, it was expected that she would perform well within the normal performance found for 2nd graders. However, this was not the case. Loraine performed poorer than 2nd graders when the background noise was meaningless speech babble. However, when there was no noise (quiet) or when the noise was a story spoken by the same person who said the words, Loraine's performance was within the norms for children in 2nd grade. Thus, Loraine has some problems understanding speech in the presence of noise, and this problem contributes to her APD (in Lucker's model identified as a deficit in auditory distractibility).

The last test administered with Loraine was the test of vigilance, the ACPT. This test has norms only going up to children 11 years of age because children at older ages perform the same as the 11 year olds. Thus, we could assume that, at least, an adult would perform at the 11 year old norm level or better. This is exactly what occurred with Loraine. She performed extremely well making only two errors of omission during the first trial and no other errors throughout the rest of the test.

When considering Loraine's performance on the audiological battery of APD tests, it was identified that she definitely has some auditory based processing problems related to background noise and pattern recognition and labeling. These problems could affect her abilities to successfully deal with auditory information. Additionally, it is probable that she has either overcome other aspects of auditory information processing that she may have had when she was a child, and had she been administered a comprehensive audiological APD test when she were younger, she may have failed more than just the parts that she failed on the testing described here.

Performance for Andrew on the Audiological Part of the APD Testing

Andrew was the reason Loraine first came in for the APD testing. Further information regarding Andrew's auditory information processing difficulties is described by Loraine in Chapter Seven and by Andrew, himself, in Chapter Six.

Andrew was administered the same tests of auditory processing as for his mother. The SCAN-A test had been used as a screening test prior to referring him on for the more comprehensive audiological assessment, and he had failed that test specifically on the Competing Words and Filtered Words subtests. Filtered Words involves processing acoustically altered words that have been electronically filtered. Competing Words is a dichotic listening tasks such as described above for the words "are" and "cow."

On the SSW Test, Andrew performed normally for his right ear, but had great difficulties repeating the words he heard in his left ear in both the non-competing and competing conditions provided on this test. Thus, Andrew was having problems with auditory lexical extraction that led to difficulties with auditory lexical integration. He was also found to have significant ear, order, reversal and Type A response biases. The ear effect goes along with the auditory lexical extraction and integration problems. The Type A has been identified by Lucker (1980 & 1982) as a problem with sound-symbol association processing that can affect the phonemic and lexical levels of processing. The order effect is related to memory deficits, so that Andrew may have memory problems, but these problems are likely related to the primary extraction and integration deficits, especially the sound-symbol association integration problem found. The reversals are related to organization and sequencing problems and Andrew's mother reported that this was definitely an area of deficit for her son.

As stated above, the Type A pattern could be related to both lexical and phonemic processing problems (extraction and/or integration). Confirmation that the problem did affect Andrew's phonemic extraction and integration came from his poor performance on the PST. He could not readily blend phonemes to form words, especially when the words had consonant blends in them.

In addition to his mother having deficits on PPST, Andrew had problems. He, too, could not pass the baseline, two tone pattern recognition and labeling section of this test. Interestingly, he scored slightly better than his mother, 75%. However, since he could not do the two tone pattern, the three tone pattern was not completed. It is assumed that if he could not do the two tone pattern, he would not have been able to do the three tone patterns.

In contrast to his mother, Andrew had no difficulties at all on the LAD Test. He scored only a few errors in the presence of both the speech babble and the story. Thus, background noise is not an interfering factor to his abilities to process auditory information (i.e., no deficits with auditory distractibility).

As with his mother, Andrew also demonstrated normal performance on the ACPT using age appropriate norms. Therefore, we can rule out a primary attention deficit as the likely factor accounting for Andrew's difficulties in processing auditory information.

If we look at all of the audiological based APD test findings for Andrew, we would realize he has problems with auditory phonemic and lexical extraction and integration, and that the problems with integration are primarily due to sound-symbol association problems. The sound-symbol association problems contribute to memory deficits, so we need to focus remediation on the sound-symbol association problems at the phonemic and lexical (linguistic) levels of processing. He also has problems with auditory temporal processing related to pattern recognition. Last, he has problems with organization and sequencing of auditory-verbal information.

Conclusion

Assessment of the auditory factors involved in auditory information processing is important for an appropriate diagnosis of APD, specifically, to find the specific areas or categories of APD that are deficient. Andrew was not identified as having any specific cognitive deficits, so we can assume that any problems with cognitive testing would be related to his difficulties with phonemic and lexical processing as well as with sound-symbol association integrative processing. The deficits identified on the SSW related to memory and organization might contribute as well to problems he has in school. However, it is likely that the auditory extraction, integration, and sound-symbol association deficits contribute to deficits in memory.

When thinking back on Andrew's information presented by Loraine and discussed by Andrew, himself, the reader may now have a better understanding of why he was having difficulties in school. The next step was to remediate these difficulties. The next chapter will discuss remediation as well as go into some specifics relative to the treatments and accommodations offered to Andrew and why they would be appropriate to his auditory information processing needs.

Chapter Ten

Treatment of
Auditory Processing Disorders

by Jay R. Lucker Ed.D., CCC-A/SLP, FAAA

C hapter Eight provided a background into how auditory information processing disorders (APD), especially the auditory based aspects of APD are assessed. From that assessment, the professional should provide enough information regarding how a treatment plan can be developed to meet the child's individual needs as well as recommendations for accommodations that can be provided to help the person with APD function at his/her best in the classroom and in any situation involving listening and communication. This chapter focuses on some of the concepts behind the specifics involved in helping children who are identified with APD. It is not a chapter specific to your child or to children with APD in general. It is important for the reader to understand that based on a categorical approach to APD, there are different types of APD problems, and the treatments and accommodations provided should be specific to the child's individual needs relative to the specific categories of APD found to be deficient for that child.

To better illustrate what is meant by specific APD, consider the following case. A child is found to be having problems listening and learning in school. The parents notice that the child has difficulties understanding verbal messages and following directions. The teachers report that the child has problems in school getting his work completed because he does not seem to understand the instructions provided by the teacher.

Cognitive testing by the school psychologist finds the child having a normal IQ with some weaknesses in verbal areas. Thus, the child's auditory information processing difficulties are not due to primary cognitive deficits. Language testing by the speech-language pathologist indicates problems with listening comprehension, but no problems with vocabulary, understanding sentence and word structure (what we refer to as syntax and morphology, respectively), and no difficulties understanding and using language in various practical, everyday social situations (what we refer to as pragmatics). Because of the listening comprehension problems from the language testing and some listening problems noted by the school psychologist, the child is seen for comprehensive auditory processing assessment by an audiologist to look at the specific auditory based APD problems.

Results of the audiological assessment indicate problems in an area this author calls auditory lexical extraction or a level at which the child has to pull out the individual, specific words from the on-going auditory message. Additionally, the child is found to have auditory temporal processing difficulties or problems at the level at which the child has to get the verbal and non-verbal (tonal) message based on time factors. Thus, spoken messages seem to be too quick for the child to get and the child becomes overloaded loosing verbal information when listening (thus having problems with auditory memory) because of the rapid speed of incoming information and his inability to pull out the key words.

Often professionals and school district teams considering what needs to provide to children with APD offer generic recommendations, such as all children failing audiological based APD tests are recommended to have an FM system. For the child in the above example, there would be no appropriate need for an FM system. The FM system would not slow down the speed of incoming verbal information making it easier for him to understand what is being said. Additionally, the FM system does not help the child know which are the important, key words in the message so the child continues to try to extract all of the words becoming overloaded and loosing information attempting to be placed into his memory store.

This example demonstrates that there is a need to look at the individual needs of the person who is having problems processing auditory information. And from understanding the individual needs, specific recommendations for accommodations and treatment can be made. This chapter discusses some of the common accommodations and treatments often recommended for children with APD, especially those identified with auditory based APD.

Accommodations

Accommodations may best be defined as those things we can provide to an individual who has APD that helps maximize his/her abilities to successfully take in and process auditory information. For example, if everyone spoke softly and whispered, and whispering were the norm, but the person with APD needed louder listening level to hear and understand spoken messages, one accommodation for that person would be that people would have to speak up and increase the volume of their voices and not whisper to the person with such an APD problem. Or some equipment might be used that increased the volume level of people's voices.

When considering which accommodations to provide the person with APD, especially children in school, we need to understand the child's specific APD problems and what techniques can be applied to overcome problems based on the child's individual APD problems. Back in the days when the adults who contributed their life stories in this book were students in school, there were few considerations provided to children with learning problems based on auditory information processing deficits. For example, Harvey describes how he had to accommodate for his learning problems and not how his teachers had to modify what they said and how they said it. Dr. J indicates one accommodation his fifth grade teacher used when teaching the children with reading difficulties. This was the use of comic books and the classics illustrated series. However, his fifth grade teacher did not have to use such tools, and could have merely continued to use the same "Dick and Jane" series of books that everyone else in class had used to learn to read.

Today, we have a better understanding that some children perform better in school when accommodations are provided to them. Both IDEA and Section 504 provide specific guidelines to include accommodations in the educational setting to meet the child's specific learning needs. The following discussion presents some of the more commonly prescribed accommodations. The reader is forewarned not to consider that each and every one of these accommodations is needed for all children with APD. As stated above, the child's individual needs must be considered when choosing which accommodations to use and when they are to be used.

FM Systems

The most commonly prescribed accommodation for children identified with APD is the use of an FM system. In general, there are two types of FM systems: sound field (or classroom) systems and personal systems. The basic components of both systems are the same.

An FM system uses FM radio frequency waves to transmit sound picked up by a microphone to a receiver that delivers the sound to the listener via some loudspeaker system. The radio frequencies used are outside the normal FM radio frequencies you would find on your FM stereo tuner. For example, we would not expect a teacher to be broadcasting her lesson on radio station 101.3 on your FM dial.

Many of us are familiar with FM transmission systems use in public address systems when we attend large meetings, such as at a religious service, or we watch singers on MTV or individuals being interviewed on some TV show. The speaker, or singer, wears a microphone that is either head worn with the microphone inlet at about the level of the mouth or the microphone is clipped onto some part of the speaker's or singer's clothing. The microphone is then connected by wire to a small box worn by the speaker or singer that houses the transmitter. You may have notice a person on an interview TV show turning around and you see a small rectangular box worn on the back of that person's pants. For a better idea of what an FM system might look like, the reader is referred to the following websites.

They are samples from different FM system companies.

Check out these websites:

http://www.boystownhospital.org/Hearing/hearingaids
/fmsystems.asp

http://www.hear-more.com/classamplification.htm

http://www.centrumsound.com/Easy_Listener.html

With an FM system, the speaker's or singer's voice is then transmitted via the FM radio waves through the air and they are picked up by an FM transmitter tuned to the same radio frequency. The receiver can be a stand alone unit with some type of antenna attached, or another small rectangular box worn by the person who is to receive the FM signal. In some systems the receiver is an integrated part of the loudspeaker through which the speaker's or singer's voice will be transmitted to the "audience." In a sound field system, the output from the receiver goes to one or more loudspeakers that are placed around the "field of sound," such as the classroom. The voice and sound received are then heard by all listeners who can hear what is coming out of the loudspeaker(s).

In personal FM systems, the loudspeakers are small headphones or earphones worn by the individual listener. Thus, only the person wearing the headphones or earphones would hear what had been broadcast via the microphone transmitter and picked up by the receiver. Today, there are a number of small receivers and loudspeakers that are built into hearing aid style devices that are worn, like hearing aids, by the individual in place of the larger headphones or even the earphones with dangling wires. These hearing aid style FM receivers have microchip technology in place of the small rectangular receiver box needed for headphones and earphones.

You may ask, "What does an FM system do?" and "Why is it helpful for people with auditory based APD?" From the above description, you should note that all that occurs in and FM system is that a speaker talks into a microphone and the voice is transmitted to a receiver and played to the group (sound field) or individual via some type of loudspeaker or earphone system. However, the receivers of FM system also house small amplifiers that boost the volume of the received sound. Thus, an FM system provides two things. First, the speaker's voice is as near to the listener as the microphone is to the speaker's lips. Thus, the speaker is speaking only a few inches from the loudspeaker's output. Second, the speaker's voice can be raised in volume to be heard comfortably without having the speaker have to yell or harm his/her voice. Other than these two factors, FM systems do not change, alter, enhance or improve the spoken message.

One additional factor provided only by personal FM systems is that they cover the listener's ears via the earphones thus blocking out sound that does not come through the microphone. It is this combination of blocking out sound, delivering speech that is only inches away from the speaker's mouth, and the ability to adjust the volume on the FM receiver that makes the FM system helpful for some children with auditory based APD. Some children with APD are bothered by the interference of background noise in the listening environment. For them, the earphones block out the background noise only when the earphones used are sufficient to block out the background noise. In the opinion of this author, all earphones used with FM systems specifically for children with auditory based APD should block out background noise, because that is the value of the FM system to improve listening in noise. Additionally, the speaker's voice, usually the teacher, is transmitted to the child's ears as the loudest sound the child will hear. Thus, the personal FM system will help the child get what the teacher is saying while blocking out background noises.

For children with auditory distractibility or problems understanding speech in the presence of noise, a personal FM system can be a successful accommodation to help them until the time when they have been taught to pull out the speaker's words from the ongoing background of noise in listening environments. Yet, this is not the only use of the personal FM system. There are also children for whom sound is too loud, even normal conversational levels of sound, and they want the sound and background noises to be reduced in volume. The use of the volume control on the personal FM system allows reduction below the normal conversational listening level, to a level that is more comfortable, for these children described as having auditory hypersensitivity. For another group of children for which sound is not recognized as something to which they should listen and process (i.e., children identified with auditory hyposensitivity) as well as children with hearing loss who, because of the hearing loss cannot readily get the sound, the use of a personal FM system delivers the speaker's voice right to their ears at a level of volume that can be adjusted to the individual listener's needs.

In the opinion of this author, it is only children with auditory based APD having problems due to auditory distractibility and auditory sensitivity for whom an FM system is needed specifically because of their APD problems. And for these children, only a personal FM system is appropriate. Sound field, or classroom, systems are helpful for all children in all listening situations as well as for teachers who do not have to strain their voices. However, a sound field FM system of any type is not appropriate specifically for a child with an APD problem.

So, you may ask, what is the value of the sound field or classroom systems? Such systems provide an amplified speaker's voice (usually the teacher) to the entire class. These systems benefit all children in the class as they all hear the teacher louder than they otherwise might hear. Additionally, an appropriately placed sound field or classroom system provides about an equal volume for the teacher's voice throughout the classroom, so a teacher walking around the room is heard equally loud by the students in front of her as by the student all the way in the back. Therefore, there is never a need to concern oneself with preferential seating (another accommodation to be discussed) based solely on the child being close to the teacher in order to hear the teacher's voice since the teacher's voice is broadcast as an amplified sound throughout the classroom.

It is the opinion of this author that all classrooms, including gymnasiums, special classrooms like art and music, and even cafeterias, be equipped with sound field FM systems. This would reduce the yelling that goes on by adults in such environments, mishearing or lack of hearing by many students, not just those with APD, and misunderstanding because of lack of hearing. However, providing sound field FM system would cost school districts and, unfortunately, money is often in short supply. Thus, we can work to obtain finances for school districts to put classroom FM systems in all new and renovated school rooms in which children will need to hear someone speaking to them.

In conclusion, then, personal FM systems are most appropriate for children with APD who have auditory distractibility problems and auditory sensitivity problems that lead to their not being able to get the primary message out of the noisy background. Additionally, sound field or classroom systems are appropriate for all students from pre-school through post graduate continuing education workshops to provide all participants equal access to the teacher's voice. Small, portable sound field systems may be useful for children working in small groups.

Preferential Seating

Another accommodation referenced above is preferential seating. This is another widely used accommodation for children with APD. When considering what is meant by preferential seating, the reader may start to realize why this accommodation, written only as preferential seating, is not sufficient in a child's IEP or 504 plan.

What is meant by preferential seating? Does it mean that the child is sitting up front while the teacher is speaking from the back of the classroom? Does it mean the teacher must have the child walk around with her in the classroom to always be near her? Or does it mean that the teacher must always be close to the child and not be able to walk around the classroom? What is meant by preferential seating is critical to providing a child with APD an appropriate accommodation.

This author feels that the preference must be spelled out. For example, Johnny is bothered by background noise, so the preference is to keep him away from noise sources. Mary has problems when there is cross talk or more than one person talking at a time, so her preference is to only have one person speaking at a time and not have her work in centers when there are many groups conversing about different things. The individual needs of the child should be spelled out when providing the accommodation of preferential seating.

Pre-Teaching

Another widely recommended accommodation is one this author calls pre-teaching. Others may call it previewing, giving the child class notes before the lecture, providing study outlines before a lesson, etc. Pre-teaching has two components to the name: "pre" and "teach." Thus, pre-teaching requires two important concepts. First is "teach." Pre-teaching means that some person sits down with the child alone or in a small group and teaches the child information predicted to be difficult for the child regarding upcoming lessons. Examples of such material would be new vocabulary, new or different language concepts, new and different ideas, and the underlying concepts that will be the base for the upcoming lesson. As part of "teach," the person doing the teaching needs to test the child to be sure he/she has learned this new material before the lesson is presented in class.

The "pre" refers to before the lesson. How far before the lesson will vary and depends on the amount and complexity of the new information to be taught as well as the child's abilities to learn the material. For some pre-teaching, the teaching has to occur only a few hours or days before the lesson. For others, it may need to be done weeks before to insure the child learns and understands the material.

The goal of pre-teaching is to provide a foundation so the child will be able to refer to the material pre-taught during the actual presentation of the lesson and not get lost or fall behind. Children with many different types of APD can benefit from pre-teaching which is why it is one of the often recommended accommodations provided by this author when he assesses APD in children. Additionally, the concepts of pre-teaching carry into adulthood. Many adults with APD would benefit from prior experience with material in lectures, workshops, seminars, etc. Some may actually benefit from pre-reading books, articles, and other material related to a topic prior to going to hear a speaker discuss that topic. In some cases, the listener with

APD can contact the speaker to get suggested readings prior to coming to the speaker's presentation on a topic.

In conclusion, pre-teaching saves time. It would appear to take time, because time must be spent in the pre-teaching of the material. However, without pre-teaching, we often have to review, re-teach, repeat, and provide extra lessons for people who have APD. Thus, pre-teaching is an accommodation that is very helpful for many children, adolescents, and adults who have APD.

Treatment for APD

There are many other accommodations we could discuss, but most of these are the same general accommodations offered to children with other types of learning problems. Other accommodations can be identified from the school team's list of accommodations that schools are typically ready and willing to provide. However, FM systems and pre-teaching are two that school districts often misuse or refuse to provide. Often the reason is economic: FM systems cost too much money to provide for one child or for one classroom; do we have the funds to pay for some person to provide the pre-teaching? This is why these two accommodations were emphasized in this chapter.

What is important for the reader to note, however, is that accommodations do not treat the APD problems. They provide for solutions to help the person until the accommodations are no longer needed. Consider the following example. A child is found to be an appropriate candidate for a personal FM system and, in first grade, such a system is provided for the child. However, no treatment is provided to teach the child how to pull out the key, important information from the background noise, and the child is now going into middle school. The child still relies on the FM system to block out the background noise and get the teacher's voice amplified through the headphones worn by the child. However, now in 6th grade, other kids are making fun of the child who is different because he is wearing headphones in class. Additionally, when there are class discussions, the child often forgets to remove the headphones and does not follow what is being discussed thus being left out of many class discussions. The question arises whether, in this case, the FM system was a help or whether it eventually became a greater handicapping disability?

What this child needed was to learn how to pull out the important, relevant message from the background noise so that, by 6th grade, an FM system would no longer be needed. This brings up an important concept that this author feels is critical to the success for young children found with APD. This concept is that the child must be provided with remediation, treatment, or services to learn the skills and strategies to overcome the identified, individual APD problems. The following discussion concerns providing treatment to children, adolescents, and adults with APD.

Teaching vs. Practice

One important concept needing to be remembered is whether the person with APD needs to learn something new or merely needs focused practice to develop, strengthen, and modify a skill or strategy already known. For example, at some point, we may teach children the alphabet and how the letters relate to their names. This may involve things like repeating the alphabet over and over and singing the alphabet song. Then, the teacher may decide to sing the alphabet song daily as well as play alphabet games, do alphabet worksheets, and even make alphabet letters out of clay. The latter activities (daily singing, playing games, and making the clay letters) provide the practice needed to reinforce the newly learned skill. Thus, both teaching and practice are needed. However, you don't want the child to practice what he/she does not know and you don't want the child to practice incorrectly. Unfortunately, many professionals and educators do not differentiate practice from teaching, and many activities people think are for teaching a skill provide nothing more than practice.

When we consider teaching a child who has an auditory information processing deficit, one important aspect is to consider what is the specific auditory information processing problem present. It is not appropriate to provide instruction or practice for a person with a language based APD using auditory based treatments and vice versa. Thus, the first factor is to get an appropriate assessment, identify what are the specific systems that are impaired and, within those systems, what areas of information processing are affected. Then we can develop a specific treatment plan, in schools called an IEP, to meet the individual needs of the child. Treatment should incorporate the child's strengths and begin at a point where the child can be somewhat successful and then build from the strengths and the level of success to new levels where the child is challenged. Once the child learns these challenges, he can move to the next stage in development, be successful, and then new challenges can be added.

Doing a Task Analysis

The first step in developing a treatment plan is to identify the goal you wish to reach with the child and the tasks needed to meet that goal. Consider driving from, say, the Washington, DC metro area to New York City (NYC). The goal is to start in the DC area and end in NYC. The tasks needed to meet that goal would include such simple things as: getting the car ready, packing any clothes/supplies needed for the journey, mapping out the trip, following the map, planning any stops along the way, and then determining how much money would be needed (for tolls, lunch, snacks that are purchased, etc.) and where the money should be kept (toll money in a handy location whereas money for lunch or snacks in a coat pocket with the coat in the back or trunk of the car). This is the same type of analysis the teacher or therapist needs to consider when developing a lesson for a child with an APD.

Let's do an example. Consider a child who has problems with auditory memory. Test findings indicate that the child's problems relate to getting the information into the memory store. Furthermore, the test data indicates that the child has a normal memory span or can hold onto the normal, age appropriate amount of auditory information so long as the child can get it into the memory system.

In doing a task analysis, we might find that it is easier to remember items when they are grouped together by category then when they are remembered as a list of individual items. We then try out a little experiment with the child having the auditory memory problem. We give the child 12 items that can be classified into three groups of four items each and merely say to the child, "Here are some pictures of things. Your job is to remember these and, later, tell me what you remember." Since the child is stronger visually then auditorily, we begin with pictures.

We then observe the child studying the cards and notice the child tries to remember each individual card, all 12 of them. After one minute of study, we put the cards aside and distract the child by asking him to count backwards from 25. When the child does this simple distraction task, we ask the child to recall as many cards as he can and find he can recall 4 of the cards.

We then teach the child the categorization task. In doing the task analysis, we realize that the steps we have used to remember by categories is first to understand the concept of categorizing. Next, we realize we remember items by just remembering their category. Last, we identify that we recall the items by recalling the categories, so all we need is to remember the category and not each individual item.

In doing this task analysis, we realize we have to teach all of these steps to the child. If this child knows how to categorize, we would start with categorizing things and then finding the different categories and ways to categorize a group of items. In this practice, we would focus on the strategy of finding multiple ways to categorize and identify which categorization method is easiest to remember. Then, we go on to the next stage which is remembering the categories and recalling the categories at a later time. Last, we work on recalling the items by first recalling the categories. Then, we practice the entire strategy with cueing and work to remove the cues by having the child independently do the memory categorization strategy alone.

This is just one example of a task analysis applied in teaching one specific strategy for auditory information processing, in this case auditory memory teaching categorization. When teaching specific strategies, the teacher, parent, or specialist working with the child needs to do a similar type of task analysis. An appropriate task analysis will lead to development of the goals and objectives in an IEP or the treatment plan. Then, the professional may choose ready made, commercially available products for the materials to be used. The following is a discussion of three commercially available products that have been used with children who have auditory information processing deficits.

Earobics

Earobics (**www.earobics.com and www.cogcon.com**) is a computer program that focuses its work in an area that might be referred to as auditory phonemic extraction and integration or auditory phonemic awareness. The company that makes Earobics, Cognitive Concepts, also has programs to practice other aspects of reading, however, the program that is most often discussed for children with auditory information processing disorders is the Earobics program: Step one, step two, and the adolescent/adult version.

Each of these Earobics programs is a CD that works on a computer allowing for the computer to track the progress for the individual using the program. There are two basic versions for each of the Earobics programs, one for home or individual use, and one for school use. The home version allows two children, plus a guest, such as the parent, to play all of the games. The school version allows for more than just two children to be tracked via one CD of the program. It also allows the teacher or professional to log in as a guest to practice with a child and to obtain information about how each individual child is performing as well as make some modifications to the availability of "games" to individual children.

All of the games on the Earobics programs focus on some aspect of phonemic awareness as well as two additional aspects. One additional aspect is auditory sequential memory. Memory is important in learning phonemic awareness and relating these skills to the reading and spelling processes. The other aspect is listening in the presence of competing, background noise.

One important concept the reader needs to remember is that merely loading the Earobics program into a computer, teaching the child how to run each program, and then having the child work on the various Earobics programs does not provide for treatment of auditory information processing problems. It is up to the professional to teach the skills and determine which of the Earobics programs is needed for any specific child. Then, the Earobics program provides systematic, practice using adaptive learning in which the task is made more difficult, easier, or remaining at a specific level of difficulty depending on how the child performs on the specific game associated with that task.

Research that has been conducted using Earobics is listed on the company's websites (provided above). The research has been contributed by a variety of professionals and school districts. The research, in general, has demonstrated significant improvements in children's reading and literacy abilities after using Earobics. Most of the research has not focused specifically on children with APD, nor with children who specifically have auditory phonemic awareness problems. The reader should also remember that Earobics is not for every child with APD and it is not a reading program. It focuses on practicing those auditory phonemic awareness skills children need to improve their reading decoding, and spelling skills. In the experiences of this author, it is one of the best programs for auditory phonemic awareness practice on the market.

Fast ForWord

As with the Earobics program, Fast ForWord (**www.fastforword. com and www.scilearn.com**) is not a single program but a family of products that also states its focuses being on improving reading skills. However, Fast ForWord goes further to claim it also focuses on improving language skills. Of the family of products involved with Fast ForWord, the programs most commonly applied with and discussed regarding children who have APD, are those that use acoustically modified sounds and speech. Checking the Fast ForWord websites can provide you with a more complete overview of these programs as well as a chance to demonstrate what some of the activities are like for the child completing the different programs.

The underlying concept behind these acoustically modified Fast ForWord programs is that children with language deficits, reading problems, and APD have underlying deficits in auditory temporal processing related specifically to the time intervals between speech sounds or phonemes in words. Consider the following.

In the word "dog," first you hear the "d" sound, then you hear a transition from the "d" to the vowel, "o," and then the "o" sound. Next, you hear the transition from the "o" vowel to the final consonant sound, "g," followed by the "g" sound. Thus, although we identify and think of "dog" as having only three phonemes, or three sounds, there are really five sounds we hear because of these two transitions. Therefore, it is hypothesized by the developers of these Fast ForWord programs the these transitions are too rapid for the child to process and, as such, if we can digitally, electronically expand the transitions, each of the phonemes will stand out easier to hear and the whole word will be easier for the child to "decode" or extract. This explains the basic concepts behind auditory temporal processing related to transitions in words. However, the same general process occurs between words and among fluid speech (sentences and paragraphs).

These Fast ForWord programs use this transition based, temporal expansion of speech by increasing the time of the transitions much longer than normal and slowly bringing the time factor back to normal so that, by the end of each "game" in the Fast ForWord program, the child is listening to speech at a normal time or temporal rate.

As with Earobics, Fast ForWord provides no specific training for the child. It is up to the professional to do teaching and use the Fast ForWord program as practice material. Research using Fast ForWord has not broken down differences in improvements made just using the Fast ForWord program without learning specific strategies vs. using the program while teaching specific strategies. This holds true for the Earobics programs as well.

Again, the reader can find much of the research that has been done with Fast ForWord at the company's website (**www.fastforword. com or www.scilearn.com**). This research has demonstrated significant improvements in reading, language, listening, and spelling skills in children. And, as with Earobics, most of the research has not specifically differentiated whether the children in the studies did or did not have auditory processing deficits and even those studies that did identify that the subjects included children with APD, they do not indicate what specific areas of auditory processing were deficient for the individual children.

The author has conducted his own research on Fast ForWord and has presented this research at professional conferences including national association conferences (Lucker 2005a, 2007a, 2008).

From the underlying factor from which Fast ForWord was developed, i.e., auditory temporal processing, the one conclusion found from this professional's research is that no significant real-life changes in auditory temporal processing were found in the subjects in his studies. This finding has been found in other studies looking at auditory temporal processing and Fast ForWord training as well. However, this professional has found significant improvements in auditory integrative processing, especially related to how the two ears work together on dichotic listening tasks. Thus, this may be the underlying improvement going on with Fast ForWord, an improvement for different parts of the brain to integrate and work more successfully together. This may also account for the improvements noted on MRI studies that have been conducted based on changes after Fast ForWord training that can be reviewed at the Fast ForWord websites.

The bottom line is that Fast ForWord is not a generic program for all children with APD. It is helpful, according to this author's research, for children with auditory integration problems that may affect reading, spelling, and language abilities. And, as with all treatments for APD, you need a differential assessment of your individual child to determine whether he/she may be an appropriate candidate for one of the Fast ForWord programs.

Lindamood-Bell Programs

The Lindamood-Bell group (**www.lindamoodbell.com and www.ganderpublishing.com**) has developed a variety of treatment programs focusing on specific underlying strategies. The goal of all Lindamood-Bell products is to teach the child specific strategies.

For example, the Seeing Stars program focuses on teaching visualization strategies using a multi-sensory approach to teach sight reading and sight spelling. It focuses much of its work on those unusual orthographic forms for words such as the "igh" combination of letters in words like light and fight. Children learn to see the letter combinations and visualize them in their heads, what this author calls "mental imagery," and then recognize the phoneme sound that goes with the combination of "igh" as rapidly as possible. Aside from this more visually based, phonics program, Seeing Stars, the auditory and language based programs from Lindamood-Bell are LiPS and Visualizing and Verbalizing or V/V. Both use visualization concepts as well as other strategies as described below.

For children with auditory phonemic extraction or phonemic awareness problems as well as sound-symbol association deficits at the reading and spelling level, the Lindamood Phoneme Sequence or LiPS Program provides strategies to help them. LiPS focuses on going back to the beginning and using a multi-sensory approach to teaching the distinctive features involved in identifying specific speech sounds or phonemes. The features are based on sound (phonemic awareness), how the phonemes look (speechreading or lipreading awareness also known as viseme awareness), and how the sounds are produced (tactile/kinesthetic awareness). Once the children learn to make these distinctive feature differentiations, the next step is to work on sound combinations and words.

At this level, a strategy is taught to relate each sound or phoneme in a word to a specific symbol using colors as the symbols. A word such as "dog" would have three phonemes, or three sounds, and, thus, three symbols. Additionally, the symbols would be three different ones, or three different colors. The word, "kite" would also have three phonemes, three symbols, and each would be different. In contrast to the spelling that uses four letters, the symbols actually are "k" "i…. e" and "t" with the "t" placed between the "i" and the "e," but the "i…. e" in the word "kite" are one symbol since they represent only one phoneme sound, what we call the long "i" vowel. This process of one phoneme = one symbol (color) continues until the child can form words with the colors and manipulate colors to form new words.

152

Eventually, the orthographic forms or letters are added as symbols instead of colors. At this point, the child is learning to read and spell, but has already learned all of the underlying processes (or steps) needed to read and spell. Thus, LiPS provides a step by step plan to teach the strategies involved.

In contrast to LiPS, that works on auditory phonemic awareness and sound-symbol associations, Visualizing and Verbalizing or V/V works on comprehension, both at the reading level as well as at the listening level. From this professional's experience, V/V also works on language development including sentence structure or syntax and expanding sentences and words in sentences.

The underlying concepts or strategies taught in V/V can be expressed as follows. Children learn to comprehend what they hear and read by visualizing the information based on the language that is used. Thus, children form mental images and, for comprehension, use the words heard or read to form, adjust, expand or change their mental images. Children learn to form the mental images and use these as a way to describe what they wish to express to improve oral and written language.

V/V also teaches the child to ask him/herself questions that Nanci Bell calls structure words as a base for forming and understanding the mental images. These structure words are closely related to the five "WH" words many teaches already use: Who/What (subject), What's happening/What's (the subject) doing, Where, When and later Why. To expand on a factor, such as the subject, the child asks questions (structure words) related to the description or attributes of the subject such as size, shape, color, number, sounds made, etc.

This author has used LiPS for many children with auditory phonemic extraction and integration problems as well as sound-symbol association problems and V/V for many children who have auditory integration and language comprehension deficits. Research on LiPS and V/V can also be found on the Lindamood-Bell website. This research also demonstrates significant improvements in reading, spelling, literacy, and language skills in children. However, much of this research has not differentiated children with of without specific APD problems.

Conclusions

The focus of this chapter has been to demonstrate that there are treatments for children with APD and that these treatments should be specific to the individual needs of the child. Often, it has been this author's experience that a shot gun or generic approach is used in which every child with APD gets the same treatment because the professional doesn't really understand APD or does not know how to obtain a differential assessment for the child.

The reader is urged to take this chapter as an overview of some of the things that can be provided to help children with APD and not as specific treatment for his/herself or his/her child. The need for an appropriate, differential assessment cannot be under stressed. It is important to find the treatment that fits the child's specific system needs and the specific category or area of auditory information processing that is impaired and is the base for the problems the child is having. Treating symptoms is like sticking your finger in the hole in the dyke. Eventually, your finger will get tired or the hole will get bigger. However, finding the specific structural problem causing the hole, fixing the structural problem along with removing the hole is the appropriate way to strengthen the dyke and lead to no further leaks. This analogy applies for children with APD.

Chapter Eleven

Resources

by Jay R. Lucker Ed.D., CCC-A/SLP, FAAA

After reading this book, you should have a better understanding of how APD can affect a person's life and education. You may have APD or know of someone with APD and be wondering where can I turn to find more information including finding a professional who assesses APD. This chapter provides an overview of resources available to parents and professionals. The chapter includes an annotated bibliography of organizations, websites, and books and other publications of interest. The review is only as up-to-date as the organizations and website managers keep them. The books and publications reflect what was available at the time of the writing of this book.

Organizations that focus on helping people with APD

There are a number of organizations that focus specifically on people with APD. Additionally there are professional organizations involving the specialists who assess and treat persons with APD. Since this book involves professionals and people in the United States, it includes a review primarily of organizations that are U.S. based. The following includes such organizations with a brief description of each. The list is presented alphabetically and does not represent any rank order of importance. Additionally, inclusion of these organizations is not meant to be an endorsement, but merely a description for your information.

American Academy of Audiology (AAA)

AAA is a national professional organization for audiologists who may provide assessments of people with APD. AAA provides information for professionals and consumers regarding their viewpoint of APD. Additionally, AAA provides a referral source to consumers to help in finding an audiologist. The referral source may not indicate whether the professional provides any work with people who have APD. You would then have to contact each professional and ask whether they provide the services you need. There is no certification or identification of specialty in auditory processing or APD from AAA.

You can contact AAA at:

11730 Plaza America Drive, Suite 300
Reston, VA 20190
800-AAA-2336 (800-222-2336)
703-790-4866 Fax: 703-790-8631
Website: www.audiology.org

American Speech-Language-Hearing Association (ASHA)

ASHA is a national professional organization for audiologists and speech-language pathologists who may provide assessments of people with APD and provide therapy for these people. ASHA provides information for professionals and consumers regarding their publications on APD including their 1995/1996 Consensus report and their most recent 2005 Technical Report and Guidelines for Audiologists providing APD assessments. Additionally, ASHA provides a referral source to consumers to help in finding one of their certified professionals. The referral source may not indicate whether the professional (audiologist or speech-language pathologist) provides any work with people who have APD. You would then have to contact each professional and ask whether they provide the services you need. There is no certification or identification of specialty in auditory processing or APD from ASHA.

You can contact ASHA at:

> 2200 Research Boulevard
> Rockville, MD 20850-3289
> ASHA Members can call 800-489-2071
> Non-member/consumers can call 800-638-8255
> Fax: 240-333-4705
> **Email:** actioncenter@asha.org
> **Website:** www.asha.org

APDUK

APDUK is an organization of professionals and non-professionals in the United Kingdom focusing on providing support and assistance for people with APD problems in the UK. They provide a website that includes their view of APD that does not differentiate APD from language processing or language disorders.

You can contact APDUK at:

> **Website:** http://www.apduk.org

Educational Audiology Association (EAA)

Since APD often affects educational issues, a number of audiologists who work with people who have APD are members of the EAA. The EAA has information regarding APD. The EAA provides information for professionals and consumers regarding their position on APD (follow links to position statements at the EAA website).

You can contact the EAA at:

> 11166 Huron Street
> Suite 27
> Denver, CO 80234
> 800-460-7322
> **Email:** eaa@imigroup.org
> **Website:** www.edaud.org

National Coalition on Auditory Processing Disorders, Inc. (NCAPD)

NCAPD is a not-for-profit, self-help, support organization comprised of parents, individuals with APD, and professionals. The NCAPD provides a referral list of professional members of the organization who state that they provide services (such as assessment, treatment, support and advocacy) for people with APD. The NCAPD does not endorse any of those listed in their referral list nor does the organization vouch for these professionals. However, this is a source for finding professionals who list themselves as providing specific work with people who have APD.

Anyone with interest in APD can join the organization that sponsors a website, e-publications and e-reprints of publications specifically on the topic of APD. The best source for contacting the NCAPD is through their website. The website contains a simulation of APD (in visual format only), links to other websites members of the organization have identified as providing meaningful information regarding APD as well as the resource list and publications/reprints referred to above.

Website: www.ncapd.org

National Institutes of Health (NIH)

The NIH is a government organization that provides research in many areas including research into issues related to auditory processing and APD. The NIH has material for professionals and consumers regarding APD. Furthermore, they periodically sponsor research involving auditory processing (AP) and APD in a variety of populations and on various aspects on AP and APD. You can contact them for information regarding any recent studies in which you may want to participate or for which you know someone who may be an appropriate candidate.

Because of its size and involvement in research, the NIH is divided into smaller institutes. The ones that may involve research on APD would include the National Institute of Child and Human Development (NICHD), the National Institute on Deafness and Other Communication Disorders (NIDCD), and the National Institute of Mental Health (NIMH).

You can contact the NIH and these institutes of the NIH at:

NIH
9000 Rockville Pike
Bethesda, MD 20892

NICHD
Public Information and Communication Branch
31 Center Drive
Bld. 31, Room 2A32, MSC 2425
Bethesda, MD 20892-2425

NIDCD
NIDCD Office of Health Communication
and Public Liason
31 Center Drive, MSC 2320
Bethesda, MD 20892-2320

NIMH
Office of Communications
6001 Executive Blvd., Room 8184, MSC 9663
Betheda, MD 20892-9663
Website: www.nih.gov

Websites Focusing on APD

APDUK

APD is not just an American thing. APD exists in other countries such as the United Kingdom (England). The UK website specializing in APD is APDUK. More on the organization and its website is described above.

www.apduk.org

Auditory Processing Disorders Down Under

This is the homepage of a parent of a child with APD who is from Australia. Demonstrates the international flavor of APD. Provides many links to other websites.

http://www.angelfire.com/home/capddownunder/

Auditory Processing Disorders Facts

This is the website of Dr. Alan B. Gertner, an audiologist who specializes in APD. He presents his views on APD with links to other websites.

http://www.homestead.com/agertner/HOMEPAGE.html

DR-J.net

This is the website of the author of this chapter who is a dually certified audiologist/speech-language pathologist and long time specialist in APD.

www.dr-j.net

Google

This popular search engine actually hosts a website specific to APD under the name Central Auditory Processing Disorders. Links are provided to other websites specifically concerning APD. However, since Google is merely a search engine, there may be no professionals or experts involved with APD that have reviewed the listening of websites.

http://www.google.com/Top/Health/Mental_Health/Disorders/ Child_and_Adolescent/Learning_Disabilities/ Central_Auditory_Processing_Disorders/

HERDEWE

HERDEWE is the website of audiologist Dr. Gary Pillow who specializes in APD. The website discusses his view and approach to APD.

http://members.aol.com/HERDEWE/

LDOnline

LD Online is a website focusing on learning disabilities and AD/HD (attention deficit/hyperactivity disorder). Since APDs often lead to learning disabilities (LD), they provide information on APD. As stated on the website, LDOnline is an educational service of the Washington, DC public TV station WETA and, thus, the material provided is not necessarily reviewed by professionals or experts in the field of APD. However, the website does provide some good information about APD.

www.ldonline.org

National Coalition on Auditory Processing Disorders, Inc. (NCAPD)

Described above, there are many links on the NCAPD website to other sites and publications concerning APD. The Board of Directors and members of the NCAPD include professionals who focus their work specializing in APD as well as highly respected experts in the field of APD.

www.ncapd.org

National Institutes on Health (NIH)

The NIH has an information website specifically regarding APD. It presents an understanding of APD from the professionals and researches at the NIH.

http://www.nidcd.nih.gov/health/voice/auditory.asp

Listserv Discussion Groups

Auditory Processing listserv list is a discussion hosted by a dually certified audiologist/speech-language pathologist, Maxine Young. The list provides an open forum for anyone joining the discussion regarding issues pertaining to APD.

http://groups.yahoo.com/group/AuditoryProcessing/

CAPD is the longest running listserv discussion hosted by the author of this chapter, a dually certified audiologist and speech-language pathologist and long-time specialist in the field of APD. This discussion list provides an open forum for anyone joining the list to discuss issues pertaining to APD.

CAPD-request@listserv.icors.org

OldAPDs

Another yahoo group listserv focusing on APD in adults. The listserv was established by the founder of APDUK who is not a professional, but an adult with APD and parent of children with APD. The list includes adults discussing issues pertaining to APD. It is an open list so anyone can join in the discussion.

http://health.groups.yahoo.com/group/OldAPDs/

Books on APD

Although there are many books written about APD, the following are books that are written at a level that even non-professionals can understand APD. Review of these books is not an endorsement of the books or their authors.

Bellis, Teri James (2003). *When the Brain Can't Hear: Unraveling the Mystery of Auditory Processing Disorder.* NY: Atria Books. ISBN: 0743428641

Written by a well-known expert in the field of APD. The book is readable by both professionals and non-professionals. The book presents the author's specific approach and conceptualization of APD.

Foli, Karen J. (2003) *Like Sound Through Water: A Mother's Journey Through Auditory Processing Disorder.* NY: Atria Books. ISBN: 074342199X

Written by a parent who claims her child has APD. Describes a mother's struggle to understand her son's communication and learning problems.

Geffner, D., and Ross-Swain, D. (Eds.) (2007). *Auditory Processing Disorders: Assessment, Management, and Treatment.* San Diego: Plural Publishing. ISBN: 159756107X

Drs. Geffner and Ross-Swain bring together some of the leading experts in the field of APD to write individual chapters covering a wide variety of topics related to definitions and approaches to assessment, treatment, and review of various programs including computer programs, Earobics, Fast ForWord, and Lindamood-Bell.

Masters, M. Gay; Stecker, Nancy; Katz, Jack, 1998, *Central Auditory Processing Disorders: Mostly Management.* MA: Allyn and Bacon. ISBN: 0205273610

Written by three well known professionals in the field of APD. Although originally written for professionals, it is easy enough to read by non-professionals.

Wright, Peter W.D., and Wright, Pamela Darr (2006). Wrightslaw: *From Emotions to Advocacy: The Special Education Survival Guide.* Harbor House Law Press. ISBN: 9781892320094

Wright, Peter W.D., and Wright, Pamela Darr (2007). Wrightslaw: *Special Education Law (2nd Edition).* ISBN: 9781892320162

Peter Wright is a highly respected educational lawyer who provides the reader, both professional and non-professional, with an excellent, comprehensive understanding of the IDEA law. Since many parents, school, and professionals are concerned with children who have APD obtaining appropriate services through the schools, this book provides an excellent background to the special education law (IDEA). Check the Harbor House Law website at:

www.harborhouselaw.com

References

American Speech-Language-Hearing Association (ASHA) Working Group on Auditory Processing Disorders (2005a). (Central) *Auditory Processing Disorders: Technical Report.* The Author (ASHA). [available on-line at **www.asha.org**]

American Speech-Language-Hearing Association (ASHA) Working Group on Auditory Processing Disorders (2005b). (Central) Auditory Processing Disorders – The Role of the Audiologist. The Author (ASHA). [available on-line at **www.asha.org**]

Bellis, Teri James (2003). *When the Brain Can't Hear: Unraveling the Mystery of Auditory Processing Disorder.* NY: Atria Books.

Chalfant, J.C., and Schefflin, M.A. (1969). *Central Processing Dysfunctions in Children: A Review of the Research.* MD: National Institute of Neurological Disease and Stroke, National Institutes of Health, U.S. Dept. of Health, Education, and Welfare, Monograph No. 9.

Chapman, C. (1993). *How to Develop Multiple Intelligence in the Classroom.* Alexandria, Virginia: IRI/Skylight Publishing Inc.

Foli, Karen J. (2003) *Like Sound Through Water: A Mother's Journey Through Auditory Processing Disorder.* NY: Atria Books. ISBN: 074342199X

Geffner, D. (2007). Central auditory processing disorders: Definition, description, and behaviors. In Geffner, D. and Ross-Swain, D. (editors). *Auditory Processing Disorders: Assessment, Management, and Treatment.* (pp. 25 - 48) San Diego: Plural Publishing.

Geffner, D., and Ross-Swain, D. (2007). *Auditory Processing Disorders: Assessment, Management, and Treatment.* (pp. 25 - 48) San Diego: Plural Publishing.

Jerger, J., and Musiek, F. (2000). Report of the concensus conference in the diagnosis of auditory processing disorders in school-aged children. *Journal of the American Academy of Audiology, 11,* 467 - 474.

Katz, J. (1992). Classification of auditory processing disorders. In J. Katz, N. Stecker, and D. Henderson (Eds.) *Central Auditory Processing Disorder: A Transdisciplinary View* (pp. 81 – 92). Chicago: Mosby Yearbook.

Katz, J. (2005). *Testing APD in Seven-Year-Old Children.* SSW Reports, 27 (3), August issue.

Keith, R.W. (Editor) (1997). *Central Auditory Dysfunction.* NY: Grune and Stratton.

Lucker, J.R. (1980). *Diagnostic significance of the Type A Pattern on the Staggered Spondaic Word Test.* Audiology and Hearing Education, 6(2), 21 – 23.

Lucker, J.R. (1982). Diagnostic significance of the Type A pattern on the Staggered Spondaic Word (SSW) Test). In Arnst, D., and Katz, J. (editors). *Central Auditory Assessment: The SSW Test – Development and Clinical Use.* (pp. 350 – 355). San Diego: Colleg-Hill Press.

Lucker, J.R. (2005a). *Working with children with auditory processing disorders.* Audio and video program for continuing education (CEU). [Available through **www.meds-pdn.com**]

Lucker, J.R. (2005b). *APD testing in children below seven years.* SSW Reports, *27*(4), November issue.

Lucker, J.R. (2007a). *Helping children with auditory processing disorders.* Audio and video program for continuing education (CEU). [Available through **www.meds-pdn.com**]

Lucker, J.R. (2007b). History of auditory processing and its disorders in children. In Geffner, D. and Ross-Swain, D. (editors). *Auditory Processing Disorders: Assessment, Management, and Treatment.* (pp. 3 – 24) San Diego: Plural Publishing.

Lucker, J.R. (2008). *Helping children with auditory processing disorders (updated).* Audio program for continuing education (CEU). [Available through **www.meds-pdn.com**]

Medwetsky, L. (2006). *Spoken language processing: A convergent approach to conceptualizing (central) auditory processing.* The ASHA Leader, 11(8), 6-7,30-31, 33.

Walsh, B (Producer), & Stevenson, R. (Director). (1964) *Mary Poppins* [Film]. Available from Disney, USA.